SCIENCE
AND CHRISTIAN BELIEF

"... Though brief in compass, Professor Coulson's book is one of the most profound studies of the relationship of science and religion that has yet been published. ..." THE TIMES LITERARY SUPPLEMENT

"... Professor Coulson, eminent in both science and Methodism, scorns "the God of the gaps", the attempt to find room for religion in science's omissions or inconsistencies: "either God is in the whole of nature, with no gaps, or He is not there at all".... It is a moving personal testimony of faith...."

THE NEW STATESMAN

Religious Books in the Fontana Series

Science and Christian Belief

C. A. COULSON
F.R.S.

*Rouse Ball Professor of
Applied Mathematics in the
University of Oxford*

COLLINS
fontana books

First published by the Oxford University Press 1955
First published in Fontana Books 1958

PRINTED IN GREAT BRITAIN

COLLINS CLEAR-TYPE PRESS : LONDON AND GLASGOW

*This book is dedicated
to the memory of my father (1879-1953)
who first showed me the unity of science
and faith*

THE McNAIR LECTURES

The John Calvin McNair Lectures were founded through a bequest made by the Reverend John Calvin McNair, of the class of 1849. This bequest became available to the University in 1906. The extract from the will referring to the foundation is as follows :

'As soon as the interest accruing thereon shall by said Trustees be deemed sufficient they shall employ some able Scientific Gentleman to deliver before the students then in attendance at said University, a course of lectures, the object of which lectures shall be to show the mutual bearing of science and theology upon each other, and to prove the existence and attributes, as far as maybe, of God from nature. The lectures, which must be performed by a member of some one of the Evangelic denominations of Christians, must be published within twelve months after delivery, either in pamphlet or book form.'

CONTENTS

In 1954 I was invited to give the McNair lectures at Chapel Hill in the University of North Carolina. The chapters of this present book represent the substance of what I said in those lectures. It was with some hesitation that I gave the lectures then, and it is with some hesitation now that I send this little book out to a wider public. For I have all too little competence to speak of the relationship between two such comprehensive beliefs as a man's science and his religion. But someone must speak, if only to assert that our science and our religion need not be at loggerheads; and that each can help the other to an enrichment of human life. Perhaps in a scientific age a professional scientist such as I am myself may sometimes be able to do this more effectively than someone with a different background. This must, I think, have been in the minds of the Committee of the McNair Fund when they invited me to give these lectures in the first place.

It would not be right to send this little volume out into the world without a few words of acknowledgment—first, to the Committee that invited me; next, to those who came to the lectures; and lastly, to all those many friends, remembered or forgotten, whose words and thoughts have helped me to formulate my own, and who should really receive any credit that may be due. My debt to them is, for me, a continual reminder of the true life of the Christian Church, and of that so often misunderstood ' communion of the Saints '.

In developing my general theme it has seemed necessary, for the sake of continuity and completeness, to repeat a part of the argument (though not of course the actual words) that I used in my Riddell lectures *Christianity in an Age of Science* at Durham in 1953. I hope that I may be pardoned for this small amount of overlapping.

Oxford 1958   C.A.C.

CHAPTER ONE

The Challenge of Scientific Thinking

THE will of John Calvin McNair was written in 1857. In providing for the endowment of these lectures it directed that their object should be " to show the mutual bearing of Science and Theology upon each other and to prove the existence and attributes, as far as may be, of God from Nature." Even at that time this was an ambitious project, as the English Bridgewater Treatises of 1829 had made clear. But the need to reconcile the new science and the old religious convictions was as real as it had ever been, as anyone could see who had read Tom Paine's *The Rights of Man* and *The Age of Reason*. Yet John McNair could scarcely have foreseen the dramatic way in which the problem was so soon to burst once more into public interest. It was in 1859 when the ink in his will had been dry for a bare two years, that Darwin's *Origin of Species* was published : it was in 1861 that Bishop Wilberforce, at a meeting in Oxford of the British Association for the Advancement of Science, so unwisely attacked this theory, and brought down upon the Christian Church the bitterness of Huxley and his followers. The complacency of the Victorian age had been shattered, and the echoes of the conflict could be heard all round the civilised world. Four years later, in 1863,

Thomas Huxley coined the phrase *Man's Place in Nature* as a title for a collection of essays on evolution : and the words themselves bear silent witness to the change that had come over the scientific community. Man's place in nature had to be seen differently now : Natural Theology required to be rethought.

It will be my object in these lectures to enquire about the propriety of holding Christian views at all, in an age so profoundly influenced by scientific discovery and scientific thought. If, as I hope to show, this is possible with complete mental integrity, then we may reasonably expect that, out of the tensions which undoubtedly exist, we shall receive a wider interpretation both of nature and of nature's God. Did not Darwin, in his *Origin of Species,* himself assert that by the new views " much light will be thrown on the origin of man and his history " ? A proper study of man's place in nature must indeed throw light not only upon nature and upon man, but —perhaps more profoundly—upon God.

It may help if I begin by outlining the way in which our thought will go. I propose first to consider the way in which our mode of life and of our thinking about it has been affected by science. This leads to a study of the tensions which we sometimes loosely refer to as the conflict between science and religion : and to a consideration of the ways in which Christians have reacted to science. As we shall see, many of these have done far more to undermine than to support the Christian interpretation. Before we can build up a satisfactory apologetic, we shall have to study the nature of scientific truth. We shall have to ask what science is trying to do, what presuppositions lie behind its practice and what is its relationship to the world of facts. Considerable changes have occurred in the last fifty years to modify the answers that might have been given earlier to some of these questions. One of the most remarkable of these is a recognition of the rôle of the scientist himself, as observer and theorist; and of the part played by the imagination. The intervention of the human element is seen to be not merely a regrettable necessity: it is central to the whole account. Nature and man share an almost wholly unexpected intimacy. This discussion prepares us for the final synthesis, in which science is admitted to be one revelation of God, consonant in its insistence on value and person with the traditional Christian concept, but adding certain elements which we could not otherwise ever know. Whether all this would really count as a " proof " of the existence and attributes of God, in the sense in which McNair directed, may be open to doubt. But both Christians and scientists are more humble now than they were a hundred years ago: and certainly few of us who have seen the wretchedness and greatness of human life through two world wars are likely to accept easy or slick answers to any of the major problems that torment us.

We must begin by recognising that Christianity claims to give an account of all that a man experiences. As Canon Raven has put it,[1] " The main process is the same whether we are investigating the structure of an atom or a problem in animal evolution, a period of history or the religious experience of a saint." Indeed are not really dealing with

Christianity unless we admit its universal competence. The falling of a stone, the nesting of a wren, the singing of a chaffinch, the affection of a dog and the effect of the shape of Cloepatra's nose on the course of history, " all are in the same volume." And that volume, which may begin with the law of gravity, goes straight on to the sense of exaltation and abasement of the human spirit before the wonder of a created universe, and it ends with Him who is God's fulness. Archbishop Temple[2] puts it even more plainly : " We affirm, then, that unless all existence is a medium of Revelation, no particular Revelation is possible." So the Christian faith links together the starry heavens above and the moral law within, and is enfeebled if it fails to do justice to either.

But science makes similar claims, though perhaps a little more restrained. T. H. Huxley could write of the power of the new knowledge : " We are in the midst of a gigantic movement greater than that which preceded and produced the Reformation." And Francis Bacon sounded the trumpet call of the era of modern science when he wrote :[3] " We need fear no lion in the path nor set any limit to our journey."

Only two possibilities are open when far-reaching claims of this kind are made by several parties. Either they go together or they are in conflict. It is true that many eminent men of science believe that their science is of a piece with their religion. But equally truly many do not. An example of the first group is my predecessor in the Rouse Ball Chair at Oxford, the late E. A. Milne, who could write[4]

The Christmas message—which is also the Christ-

ian message—is "Gloria in excelsis Deo" . . .
Glory to God in the highest and on earth peace
among men of goodwill. This is not a bad definition of the aim of all true science; the aim of rejoicing in the splendid mysteries of the world and
universe we live in, and of attempting so to understand those mysteries that we can improve our
command over nature, improve our conditions of
life and so ensure peace.

But side by side with that let me put the assertion of
an American Professor of physiology; that " science
has shown religion to be history's cruellest and wick-
edest hoax." It is evident that we are called to do
some more thinking about this matter. The need for
such re-thinking has grown precisely in so far as
science has begun to influence man's response to his
environment; and this influence has recently been
developing at a rapid rate. In his Reith lectures for
the British Broadcasting Corporation in 1953, J. R.
Oppenheimer[5] could say without fear of contradiction : " Science has changed the conditions of man's
life . . . the ideas of science have changed the way
men think of themselves and of the world." My
former friend and colleague at Oxford, the late Professor Sir Francis Simon, could begin the preface to his
latest book :[6] " The world to-day is moulded, in the last
resort, by scientific discovery . . . whether we like it or
not, science is forcing the pace." And perhaps more
significant than any of these, a former president of the
Carnegie Endowment for International Peace can
compare the rise of science with other regulative
factors in people's lives, and can say : " The greatest

event in the world to-day is not the awakening of
Asia, nor the rise of communism—vast and porten-
tous as those events are. It is the advent of a new
way of living, due to science, a change in the conditions of work and the structure of society which began
not so very long ago in the West, and is now reaching out over all mankind." Perhaps this is why the
President's Scientific Research Board in 1946 could
speak of science[7] as " a major factor in national survival."

It is not only scientists who speak in terms like
these. Thus Herbert Butterfield,[8] professor of history
in the University of Cambridge, can say in his *Origins of Modern Science* : The scientific revolution
of the sixteenth and seventeenth centuries " outshines
anything since the rise of Christianity and reduces the
Renaissance and the Reformation to the rank of mere
episodes, mere internal displacements within the system of medieval Christendom." So also Professor G.
M. Trevelyan, the author of *English Social History,*
could write a few years ago : " There is too little
about science in our histories, considering that science
has been the chief factor in human affairs, and particularly English affairs, during the past 200 years."
Yet this change in our way of thinking is really all
very sudden. It was not until the end of the nineteenth century that large-scale professional science
grew up to use and adapt and develop the work of
the " great amateurs " of the preceding century. It is
a sobering thought to remember that the term " scientist " was unknown until William Whewell, Professor
of Moral Philosophy and Master of Trinity, Cam-

bridge, deliberately coined it in the nineteenth century.

This growth of science was tumultuous: and it was progressive. Herein lies a large part of the origin of our problem. For if the scientific revolution had come gradually, we might have been able to adapt our older views so as to contain the new. But as things turned out, this was not possible: and in the process of building a new way of thought, science destroyed the old. It is surely no exaggeration to say that the loss of tradition—of whatever kind—throughout the world, is largely an accompaniment of the rise of science. In one sense—though we shall have much more to say about this in a later chapter—science and tradition are opposites. Michael Foster[9] has recently illustrated this by a consideration of the toothpaste which he normally uses. On the tube it describes itself as a "scientific dental cream." Now what does it mean when a manuufacturer puts on the dental cream that it is "scientific"? It means that it has not been made by the "carrying out of traditional processes learned from his father, and handed down from *his* forefathers. It has not been done traditionally, but in a different way, a scientific way." Our advertisement hoardings are crowded with similar illustrations.

No account of science is fair unless it does justice to this amazing vitality and growth. It is scarcely to be wondered at that there has seemed to many to be an open conflict with conventional religious views. For if we "set no limit to our journey" it is almost inevitable that there will be tensions.

"The scientific spirit," said Freud, "engenders a particular attitude to the problems of this world; before the problems of religion it halts for a while, then wavers, and finally here steps over the threshold. In this process there is no stopping. The more the fruits of knowledge become accessible to men, the more widespread is the decline of religious belief, at first only of the obsolete and objectionable expression of the same, then of its fundamental assumptions also. The Americans," he concludes, "who instituted the monkey trial in Dayton have alone proved consistent."[10]

I want to stress this dynamic character of science. For without recognising it, we cannot see the power which it wields. Sir Richard Gregory, for many years the editor of our scientific journal *Nature*, once wrote his epitaph. It begins as follows:

> My grandfather preached the gospel of Christ,
> My father preached the gospel of Socialism,
> I preach the gospel of Science.

There is good and bad in this; and the last thing which I want to do is to pour scorn on it. This, as we shall see later, would be quite fatal. For the moment we must be content to trace this growth of influence, and see where it is leading us. For some, it is a liberating influence, pregnant with possibility. "The next great task of science," said Lord Morley, "is to create a religion for mankind." For others it will be destructive, and so far from creating a religion, will destroy it. Such a view finds its clearest

enunciation among the Communists, but it is a
strange irony of fate that its next stronghold is among
the technicians of the more highly industrialised
nations in Europe and America. Karl Heim[11] has
illustrated this very clearly from official Communist
pronouncements. Thus on 28 June 1948, *Pravda,* the
central organ of the Communist Party in Russia,
published a series of titles for scientific lectures directed against the widespread revival of religious
" superstitions." Among them was this : " Every
religion contradicts science." Apparently, in order to
overthrow religious faith, all that was needed was for
scientific workers to give lectures about the construction of the universe, the origin of the sun and the
earth, the biological origins of man and plants, and
so on. Professor Togerow could write in the army
newspaper *Red Star* : " The relics of religious faith
must be wiped out by systematic scientific propaganda." And there is no doubt about the results of
such propaganda. Commenting on these Press notices, Heim points out the significant thing about
them, that

here is not just a battle about a proper world-view,
with an irreligious version of the world and its
process set against religious faith. The point of
view presupposed by the titles is that the matter
no longer calls for discussion. It will be enough if
the generally accepted scientific facts established
by research are made known to people. The religious notions . . . will then disappear of themselves,
like phantoms of the night when the day dawns.

If we are inclined to write all this off as merely Communist propaganda, we shall be making a profound mistake. We might do well to remember that Joseph Butler, in the Advertisement prefixed to the first edition of *The Analogy of Religion,* wrote : " It is come, I know not how, to be taken for granted, by many persons, that Christianity is not so much as a subject of enquiry; but that it is now at length discovered to be fictitious."

It is important to realise that in this summary of some of the influences of a scientific view, we have passed far beyond mere technology or gadgeteering. We may begin there, because that is about as far as the man-in-the-street, or the young apprentice at his lathe, can state his beliefs. But his unrecognised convictions go much deeper. For he knows that science grows, even though he may have no personal knowledge of any of its fundamental principles; and he knows that scientific controversy nearly always issues in universal agreement, frequently very quickly. Science becomes the cohesive force in modern society, the ground on which may be built a secure way of life for man and for communities. It was an American sociologist[12] who wrote :

This is why, if one wants to understand the culture of the United States, one must not look at its departments of economics, sociology or politics, important as they are, but at its universal education in the natural sciences and their skills, its agricultural colleges, technological institutes and research laboratories.

We may be tempted to smile at a certain naïveté in all this. But it springs from convictions much deeper than we sometimes recognise. For it must seem to many that within science there is such understanding of man, and his place in the scheme of things, such power to create and to destroy, such magnificence of pattern and splendour of success, that it can fulfil the deepest urges and longings of man's spirit, in a way which established religion has not been able to do. This, which is sometimes called the scientific attitude, has been well expressed by C. H. Waddington.[13] " Science itself, and so far as I can see, only science by itself, unadulterated with any contrary ideal, is able to provide a way of life which is firstly self-consistent and harmonious, and secondly is free for the exercise of that objective reason upon which our civilisation depends." And elsewhere : " At the present time only science has the vigour, and the authority of achievement, which is necessary to give them that fresh vivacious *joie de vivre* which captivates men's hearts and minds." If we are to restore faith to men, it will be through science. Perhaps this is why on 1st January, 1954, my daily newspaper, after describing a new form of surgical operation in which a large part of the body was kept at almost freezing temperature while an external pump was used to circulate the blood and by-pass the heart, which could then be operated on, could announce the arrival of the New Year in these terms : " We have just entered the eighth year of the Atomic Age."

What can have happened to bring about such a situation as this ? For certainly that was not the atmosphere within which modern science grew up.

As people like Herbert Butterfield and A. N. Whitehead[8] have shown convincingly, science grew up
within a Christian tradition : and for many years it
was in no sense distinct or separate. The founder of
science at Oxford, in the early thirteenth century, was
Robert Grosseteste, author of a *Compendium Scien-
tiarum* and later Bishop of Lincoln. He had no hesitation in saying that it was " impossible to understand
Nature without experiment or describe her without
geometry " (or, as we might say now, theoretical
physics); and by this he implied the unity of science
and faith, just as much as his distinguished pupil, the
Somerset Friar Roger Bacon, whose *Opus Maius,*
written at the request of Pope Clement IV, was de-
signed to show that the new knowledge, so far from
being an enemy of Christian faith, was actually an aid,
even in the business of evangelising mankind. This
was because it could " assist the Church . . . by leading the mind through a study of the created works
to a knowledge of the Creator." Indeed, arithmetic,
even in the new Arab notation just coming into
vogue, was something in the nature of a necessary
study for theologians, who, he says, should " abound
in the power of numbering."[14]

This same wholeness of outlook lasted well into the
beginnings of modern science. Our Royal Society
was founded in 1645, and to its growth and importance much of the dissemination of knowledge, without which science cannot live, is due. Among its
members were John Wilkins and Seth Ward, both
bishops; John Wallis, doctor of divinity and mathematician; Robert Boyle the chemist who bequeathed
the sum of £50 a year to found a lectureship for

" proving the Christian religion against notorious in-
fidels," and " chiefly recommending his dear sister "
(his executor) to " the laying of the greatest part of
the same " (i.e. his personal estate) " for the advance
or propagation of the Christian religion among in-
fidels ";[15] John Ray, the founder of systematic botany
and zoology, whose great book *The Wisdom of God
Manifested in the Works of Creation* exercised a profound influence among thinking people and was even
used in a shortened form by John Wesley in training
his travelling preachers; Christopher Wren, astronomer and architect of St. Paul's Cathedral; as well
as the greatest figure of them all, Isaac Newton, who
claimed (though we might perhaps disagree with him
in this) that his theological studies were at least as
important as his strictly scientific ones. It may be
true that religious discussions as such were not permitted at meetings of the Society; but in their second
charter, the Fellows were commanded to direct their
studies " to the glory of God the Creator, and the
advantage of the human race." And any doubts
regarding the relation between the Society and the
Church were to be dispelled by its first historian,
Sprat, who wrote :

I do here in the beginning most sincerely declare
that if this design (of a Royal Society) should in the
least diminish the reverence that is due to the
doctrine of Jesus Christ, it were so far from deserv-
ing protection that it ought to be abhorred by all
the politic and prudent, as well as by the devout,
part of Christendom.

Of course we know how the separation developed; it
was an inevitable result of the atomisation of knowledge. We know that there was a time once when
religion, morals, science and aesthetics all owned a
common discipline. As its name implies, geometry
grew up among the priests of Egypt to meet the difficulties of land measurement following periodic
floods in the Nile valley. Astronomy arose, perhaps in
Babylon, to fix the times of sacred festivals. In England, for centuries medicine and nursing were the
work of monks and nuns; St. Bartholomew's is the
oldest hospital. Practically all our older schools, as
well as the greater part of Oxford and Cambridge,
are religious foundations.

But all this has gone—gone with the coming of
that differentiation of function which accompanied
the rise of civilisation and led to the growth of many
separate disciplines, where one had served before.
No longer, as in the period 1640-1890 at Harvard, is
psychology to be classed as a sub-division of physics,
known as pneumatics (or pneumatology)! It was a
necessary stage in our intellectual development that
this specialisation should intervene to break the previous unity. When we build our University physics
laboratories to-day, we no longer adorn their main
gateways as the gateway of the Cavendish Laboratory
at Cambridge is adorned: "The works of the Lord
are great: sought out of all those that have pleasure
therein." In fact, when the Royal Society Mond
Laboratory for low temperature research was opened
at Cambridge in the 1930's it was the carving of a
stone crocodile that decorated its entrance. However
symbolic the choice (and it was symbolic) we can

hardly fail to be struck by the difference. There is no need to describe how, stage by stage, this difference has become accepted. It is an old story and well known. First the age of the earth, then the mechanism of biology, the theory of evolution, the growing control of power and energy, the harnessing of the elements, the understanding of the nervous system and the brain, these are just a few of the highlights in the process. God was found an unnecessary hypothesis in one after another field of study and experience, until He seemed to have become a silent actor in the play, scarcely needed even to present Himself upon the stage.

" The whole history of modern science," says Professor J. D. Bernal,[16] " has been that of a struggle between ideas derived from observation and practice, and preconceptions derived from religious training. It was not that Science had to fight an external enemy, the Church; it was that the Church —its dogmas, its whole way of conceiving the universe—was within the scientists themselves. After Newton, God ruled the visible world by means of Immutable Laws of Nature, set in action by one creative impulse, but He ruled the moral world by means of absolute intimations of moral sanctions, implanted in each individual soul, reinforced and illuminated by Revelation and the Church. The rôle of God in the material world has been reduced stage by stage with the advance of science, so much so that He only survives in the vaguest mathematical form in the minds of older physicists and biologists. In physics He is needed only to explain the creation of a universe which is discovered, as research advances, to be less and less like the one with which we are familiar. In biology He is invoked to account both for the origin of life, and for the purpose of evolution. Now the history of scientific advances has shown us clearly that any appeal to Divine Purpose, or any supernatural agency, to explain any phenomenon, is in fact only a concealed confession of ignorance, and a bar to genuine research."

It is a striking paragraph : but we shall do well not to dismiss it in too facile a manner. For there has been far too much " concealed confession of ignorance " in the traditional Christian apologetic for any of us to feel easy about the strictures which Bernal passes upon us.

It may help us to see this more clearly if we think for a moment of some of the more common faults in the approach of the Christian to scientific knowledge. Most of these major mistakes are not difficult to discern. But when we see them, as it were collectively, we can begin to appreciate the difficulties that we place in the way of some of our more serious scientific thinkers.

First—and easiest—is a clinging to the past. This is the attitude of mind of those who cannot face the implications of new knowledge, and insist on some sort of nostalgic return to things as they were. It is an attitude born of fear, and almost entirely unproductive. It is certainly the antithesis of the scientific attitude, and it lacks such elasticity of mind as is required if we would deal creatively with any new influx of knowledge or experience. This is the frame of mind in which Bishop Wilberforce tried to deal with Darwin's *Origin of Species,* spouting " for half an hour with inimitable spirit, ugliness and emptiness and unfairness " at that famous Oxford meeting of the British Association, and later, when writing about the book in the *Quarterly Review,* declaring that " the principle of natural selection is absolutely incompatible with the word of God," since " evolution was an attempt to dethrone God "; this is because if its thesis is true, " Genesis is a lie, the whole framework of the book of life falls to pieces, and the revelation of God to man, as we Christians know it, is a delusion and a snare."[17] It is the frame of mind of the Dean of York who, only thirteen years after the British Association had been founded, in his own city, and very largely as the result of efforts by professing Christians,[18] could reflect upon the difficulties raised by recent geological research, and write a pamphlet with the vituperative title : *The Bible defended against the British Association.* So well did the excellent Dean represent public opinion that this pamphlet went through several editions in the first year of its publication. It is one of the great tragedies of this dispute that some of the finest exponents of Christian faith have fallen victim to this disease, this hardening of the arteries of Christian thinking. Here, for example, is Martin Luther, only a few years after Copernicus had published his *De revolutionibus orbium coelestium* in 1543, speaking of its author as a new astrologer wanting to prove " that the Earth is moved and goeth around and not the Sun," a view which he stigmatised as " the over-witty notion of a

Fool, who would fain turn topsy-turvy the whole Art
of Astronomy."[19]

It was precisely because, in all these cases—the
theory of evolution, the age of the earth, the helio-
centric account of astronomy—current views were
being turned topsy-turvy, that it was necessary to
maintain an elasticity of mind. Had they but realised it, all three of these " over-witty notions " were
a liberating influence, opening up new possibilities of
understanding the nature of God's universe, and Him
who made it. And so, as we cling to the past, we let
the golden opportunity roll by, and we build up for
the next generation a barrier of mistrust and concealed ignorance. There is no hope for the ostrich,
with its head buried in the sand.

The examples just given are not by any means
exhaustive, nor do they cover all the varieties of
retreat which have been chosen. I want to include
here the attempts to take refuge in metaphysics—a
situation which seems not infrequently to follow the
discovery that physics itself is not sufficiently accom-
modating to our personal whim. Here, for example,
is William of Auvergne (died 1249) arguing that the
world cannot possibly have existed from eternity.
For, he says, suppose that the revolutions of Saturn
stand to the revolutions of the sun in the proportion
of one to thirty; then the sun will have made thirty
times as many revolutions since creation as Saturn.
But if the world exists from Eternity, both Saturn
and the sun will have made an infinite number of
revolutions. Now how can infinity be thirty times
another infinity?[20] We laugh at this now, and
rightly : we put it on the same level as the argument

that since there are four points of the compass there can only be four gospels; or that since there are seven openings in the head, there can only be seven planets. But this type of argument remains, and causes a quite unnecessary confusion.

For example Karl Heim, in his monumental *Der Evangelische Glaube und das Denken der Gegenwart*[21] argues quite correctly that modern theoretical physics has shown us that we may no longer think in terms of an absolute object, absolute mass, absolute rest, or absolute time. Then he goes on to assert that since we have lost all our previous absolutes, we are left with only one possibility, an absolute God. I am not surprised that his whole argument begins by an attempt to set up a "reality beyond the reach of scientific investigation,"[22] nor that he begins his fifth volume[23] by saying that "if we wish to investigate the relation between faith in God and the theses of modern natural science, we require an origin from which to plot the enquiry, just as a circle must have its origin immovably fixed in order that its circumference may be plotted in a given plane. The fixed point," he continues, "from which we must begin can be none other than God." Such defence of the faith may sound well in certain types of ear : but it cuts no ice with the professional scientist who feels hamstrung right away when told to accommodate his science to some reality beyond his reach. The only hope for science, as it is certainly its glory and excitement, is to follow uncompromisingly wherever we are led, into whatever abyss or on to whatever height, and accept whatever we may meet upon the way. Huxley's reply to the ill-fated Bishop Wilberforce in that famous meeting at Oxford, deals most devastatingly with such attempts at synthesis: "I am come here in the interests of science." We may be tempted to hesitate before we use such words ourselves; but if science is a revelation of God, there is nothing impious or false about them: and the breath of fresh air that they bring blowing with them will be useful in sweeping away the cobwebs of metaphysical dogmatism.

There are plenty of other examples of this procedure. I have already quoted approvingly from my distinguished predecessor E. A. Milne. But now I find myself protesting. In his posthumous *Modern Cosmology and the Christian Idea of God*[24] he describes possible ways in which the universe might have originated: and he deals with some of the difficulties implicit in the application of the theory of relativity to this problem. Essentially the difficulty arises from the idea of simultaneity. Einstein's great contribution was to show that there was no satisfactory operational significance to be given to the concept of simultaneity, as a result of the finite speed of light, which requires time for one observer at one point to tell his friend at another point that something had just happened. It therefore becomes an interesting problem, to ponder how any sort of Creation could have taken place "at one moment of time." If the Universe was large, you could not speak in any operationally meaningful way of "one moment" common to every part of it. There are of course other difficulties about a universe which began at a single point, as the theories of Eddington and Le Maître and others have suggested. And similar difficulties are associated with the more modern concept of continuous creation, due to Bondi, Hoyle and Gold.[25] But this is what Milne said about this situation :

> Again, we saw that the creation of the universe demanded creation at a point singularity. For the creation by God of an extended universe would require an impossibility, the impossibility of the fixation of simultaneity in the void—impossibility, that is, to a rational God. The paradox follows, that the Deity Himself, though in principle all-powerful, is yet limited by this very rationality. With God all things are not possible. This equality rules out the idea of continuous creation of matter everywhere in space, for there would have to be a pre-created space in which the creation of matter could take place; and there would exist a constant, namely the rate of creation of such matter, which could not be rationally accounted for.

All this will not do. Some metaphysical views about point singularities and simultaneity have been made to impose conditions on the nature of God. John Calvin McNair bade his lecturers " prove the existence and attributes as far as may be, of God from Nature." But this seems to me like using some preconceived view of Nature to limit or restrict His operation. Our task is not to bury Caesar, but to praise him.[26]

I have still not said everything that there is to say about the commoner faults in Christian thinking with regard to science. It has always been one of our major temptations to try to divide our experience into two (or more) parts and grant science control of the one part, while allowing religion to maintain its authority in the other. This is a fatal step to take. For it is to assert that you can plant some sort of hedge in the country of the mind to mark the boundary where a transfer of authority takes place. Its error is twofold. First it presupposes a dichotomy of existence which would be tolerable if no scientist were ever a Christian, and no Christian ever a scientist, but which becomes intolerable while there is one single person owning both allegiances. And second it invites " science " to discover new things and thence gradually to take possession of that which " religion " once held. In some respects I believe this to be the most serious and wasteful of all our errors. For we cannot hope to maintain a series of hedgehog positions on the battlefield, while all the time the enemy is pouring his energy and his forces into the region behind us. There is no " God of the gaps " to take over at those strategic places where science fails; and the reason is that gaps of this sort have the unpreventable habit of shrinking. When Descartes located the soul in the pineal gland, all was well until the real purpose of this particular gland was discovered. Then there was no room for the soul, and people began to doubt whether there really was such a thing. What is more, even when it was there, it was hard to see why it was not subject to familiar physiochemical laws. It was just the same when Newton, trying to apply his splendid discovery of the law of gravitation to as many different problems as possible,

and finding that although it would deal with the
motion of the moon round the earth, and the earth
round the sun, it would not deal with the spinning of
the earth around its polar axis to give us night and
day, wrote to the Master of his Cambridge College,
Trinity : " the diurnal rotations of the planets could
not be derived from gravity, but required a divine
arm to impress it on them." This is asking for
trouble. For as soon as any one possible scheme is
devised whereby the planets might conceivably have
obtained their angular momentum, the " divine
arm " ceases to be needed; science has asserted its
ownership of that much new territory.

We might have expected that the unwisdom of this
type of intellectual partitioning would have been
widely recognised. But that does not seem to be the
case. Here, for example, is the author of a recent
book on *Christian Faith and the Scientific Attitude*[27]
pondering on the statistical character of modern
physics, and trying to draw up hopeful lines of defence with its aid :

> " I am myself inclined to think that the mystery
> of God's providence lies deeper than the eruption
> into nature of such interferences " (he is thinking
> of the possible control of matter by mind). " And
> I am attracted by the fact that scientific explana-
> tions and predictions rest now on the ' law of great
> numbers '; that the fundamental physical laws are
> statistical and not exact in the popular sense. Why
> this should be so is an interesting matter for specu-
> lation. It may provide a sufficient room for

manoeuvre, beneath the observable regular processes, for the personal care of God to be actively
exercised."

I do not know what other people will want to say
about that sort of argument. But I know what I
want to say myself—that a God who is obliged to
conceal His actions of providence so that we cannot
see Him, a God who hides His presence in Nature
behind the law of large numbers, is a God for whom
I have no use; He is a God who leaves Nature still
unexplained, while He sneaks in through the loopholes, cheating both us and nature with His disguised "room for manoeuvre." I feel like Charles
Kingsley after he had read the *Omphalos* of Philip
Gosse, with its curious solution of the reconciliation
of geology and Genesis whereby, at God's command,
the whole natural order burst into full perfection,
during the space of six days, with the fossils all con-
veniently arranged in layers, and the trees having a
sufficient number of yearly rings, so that despite their
new birth they resembled growths of varying ages.
To believe this, said Kingsley, is to believe that God
has planted a deliberate lie. Creation as one act at a
particular time "tends to prove this, that if we
accept the fact of absolute Creation, God becomes a
deceiver."

I feel much the same about some words from one
of our most distinguished astrophysicists,[28] when he
speaks of the "notion of God continually interven-
ing, with deft touches now here, now there, to direct
the material particles in the universe so as to conform
to rationally deduced laws." For if God's action in

nature is limited to "deft touches here and there," I can barely distinguish Him from the engineer who made the mechanism, and now leaves it to work its own passage, interfering only to put it right when something is going too far wrong. Either God is in the whole of Nature, with no gaps, or He's not there at all.

This discussion leads me to the last of the points that I must make in this preliminary analysis. It is closely related to what I have just said about the futility of marking out regions of science distinct from regions of religion. But now, instead of trying to find loopholes within science, which we could hang on to in the name of religion, we admit the regional character of either account, and bravely try to use the incompleteness of science as a "proof" of religion; we look for specific places where science comes to a stop because it is leading us to a region where it has no territorial rights. This point of view fails for precisely the same reason that its predecessor failed—our experience from history that the boundary once defined, does not remain: that territorial rights are established where they used not to be allowed: that instead of leading to belief in a new order which takes over where the old order ceases to apply, we are actually led to conclude that there is no permanent boundary, and, in time, only one suzerainty. We cannot serve God and Science, when the antithesis is put in such terms as these. God must be found within the known, and not the unknown.

Here are some examples to show the sort of thing that I mean. A most distinguished experimental physicist is talking about causality, and the principle of indeterminacy, due to Heisenberg, which appears to be related to it. After noticing that if we can never measure the position and velocity of an electron (or any other particle either) with complete accuracy, so that we can never have any hard and rigid determinism of the kind that was fashionable seventy years ago, he asks the question : Are we therefore to abandon the idea of causality, or should we suppose that God takes control by means of causes that we shall never fully comprehend?

" It is for me easier," he writes, "to suppose that there are causes that elude, and must for ever elude, our search, rather than to suppose that there are no causes at all. . . . In short we must admit causes beyond our comprehension. The electron leads us to the doorway of religion."[29]

This is really a most remarkable statement. The first part is sheer metaphysics, and illustrates my argument about the folly of letting such considerations intrude into this controversy. And the second part, in which the electron leads us from a region labelled " science " to the doorway of another region labelled " religion," illustrates my claim that science will itself destroy the ground of belief in religion, when it is urged in this territorial fashion. This particular issue is an important one, and warrants a somewhat fuller description than some of my other illustrations, in view of the wide use which has been made of Heisenberg's uncertainty principle in ways like this. The problem hinges on what is implied by the statement that an electron has momentum (or velocity) and position. When we use language of this sort, we have in mind the picture of a small billiard ball which by analogy with larger billiard balls we ought therefore to be able to describe in terms of momentum and position. But why should an electron be like this? The plain truth is that we don't know. There is no finally convincing ground to justify us in calling it a particle at all. It is true that we find it exceedingly convenient for many purposes to treat it as if it really were a particle : but there are other occasions when it is far more convenient to treat it as if it were something quite different, about which we may use the language of waves and wavelengths and frequencies. In this second language position and momentum do not have the same meanings as when we are using the billiard ball picture. The uncertainty principle applies to both languages. In the particle language it tells us that there are limits to the precision of our measurement of position and velocity. In the wave language it speaks of limits to measurement of frequency and time. The uncertainty principle says nothing at all about whether we should use the one language or the other; i.e. whether there really is a particle with a position and a momentum. This is an undecidable question, and probably in the last resort it has no meaning to ask it. The clue to the whole problem is quite simple and straightforward once we realise that the uncertainty principle only talks about the results of measurement. It says nothing about the validity or otherwise of the model which we are using. Here the considered judgment of the physicists after twenty-five years thinking about it, is that the arbitrariness of a wave or a particle description warns us that we must enlarge our concepts. An electron is not a particle, though it may be good enough for many purposes to treat it as if it were. An electron is not a wave, though again for certain other purposes it may be convenient to treat it as if it were. This means that the electron does not lead us to the gateway of religion : it leads us to think a little more deeply about our science, and to modify our fundamental concepts to bring them into line with the increasing variety of our experiments. Once we admit that the electron need not be pictured as a tiny particle, the uncertainty relation has nothing more to say about freewill.

There is one other example of this misuse of science which I must mention since it occurs so frequently. I am referring to the field of parapsychology and extra-sensory perception. The confusion here is quite astonishing. For example, the Wykeham Professor of Logic at Oxford in his recent seventh Eddington Memorial Lecture,[30] when speaking of the conflict between science and religion, begins by arguing "that the crucial issue in this long-standing controversy is nothing more or less than human personality. Two apparently irreconcilable answers are offered to the old question 'what is man?' I shall suggest," he continues, "that psychical research is the one line of inquiry which seems likely to throw fresh light on the dispute." I shall myself attempt to show, in a later chapter, that the first half of this assertion is dangerously incomplete, since it is man himself who both asks and answers and judges the question "what is man?" And as for the second half, what psychical research is likely to do will be to throw more light, not on the so-called dispute between science and religion, but on the conclusions of science in the matter of time and space.

We can see this very clearly if we consider the implications of some of the exciting studies recently carried out by Professor J. B. Rhine.[31] Most of us are now familiar with the outline of this work, in which some form of telepathic communication is established,[32] sometimes across large distances: or in which it is shown that a suitable receiver, by the exercise of his will, can apparently alter the falling of a dice (Psychokinesis); or can read a pack of cards upside down with an accuracy whose random probability is so exceedingly minute that we can hardly escape the inference that some extra-sensory perception is involved. When all this has been established it is very tempting to claim that we have scientific evidence either for the existence of some sort of soul, or for a relationship between two minds which is not subject to the laws of physics. Not a few people make this claim, though it is sheer folly to do so. This, for example, is how one devotee writes about the whole matter.[33]

It seems impossible to account for the relationship of extra-sensory perception and psychokinesis to space and time by physical laws. Similar results are obtained whether the distance involved is a few feet, or thousands of miles. This fact rules out any physical explanation for telepathy, such as that of electric waves emitted by one brain being received by another. Also, the displacement in time in the form of precognition makes such an

explanation invalid. Orthodox Christians have
always accepted on the authority of the Bible that
there is something which transcends time and
space, but now, for the first time, it has been
proved by careful laboratory experiments. The
Christian will thank God that some of those things
which he believed have now been proved by
modern investigation.

When we read this, we ought to ask ourselves precisely what has been proved by these experiments. It
may be true that, if the results of these experiments
are as they are claimed, we have shown that there is
something which " transcends time and space." But
that only means time and space as we interpret them
at this moment. It is easy to see the main outline of
what will happen when these most interesting results
are fitted into the general scheme of physics. They
will become the basis on which we build a revised
model of time and space. St. Augustine[34] tells us
that time exists only in ourselves, and as long ago as
1710 Bishop Berkeley[35] had rejected the idea of
" pure space " as a " pernicious and absurd notion."
The story of physics is simply full of changed models
for space. At one period space is a plenum, full of
vortices or their equivalent: at a later time it is
empty: then it is the seat of electric and magnetic
forces: next it is an aether: under Einstein's influence it becomes curved; the quantum theoreticians
now load it full with zero-point vibrations and imaginary oscillators.[36] Whenever any new phenomenon
has appeared and has been found not to fit with
previous models of space or time, the model has been

changed—generalised in such a way that the old is not destroyed or thrown away: but the new is built on to it in such a way that we know under what conditions we do not need to concern ourselves with the change, and under what conditions the alterations are decisive. This is what will happen once more, when the experimental works of Professor Rhine and the Society for Psychical Research are finally accepted into the main body of science. Our model of space and time will be suitably adapted to "make sense" of the new situation. Before we become too enthusiastic in "thanking God" for this discovery in psychic behaviour, we should do well to ask ourselves whether it does really force us to believe in God in a manner different from all other experience. Thinking of what has happened in the past, and will probably happen in the future, we may well hesitate. It was the Marquis de Laplace who was reproached by Napoleon for failing to mention God in his great treatise on celestial mechanics. His reply—absolutely crushing and utterly correct, was simply this—" Sire, I have no need of that hypothesis." Yet it was a practising Christian who spoke those words. If we follow the types of Christian apology that I have tried to describe in this account, whether looking for some metaphysical argument to impose God on science, or trying to find some " God of the Gaps " to complete what we believe science can never succeed in doing, or attempting to use science as an escalator carrying us smoothly to that particular part of the building where religion is housed, then we must not be surprised if the scientist turns round to us and says: " If that is the best you can say about

God, I don't think I'm very interested. For within that framework He is a hypothesis for which I have no need: and for which you too will have no adequate justification when science has progressed a little further than it has to-day."

The plain truth of the situation, for which we ought to be profoundly glad, is simply this: he's right. If we would find God in science, we must begin again. But that must wait to the next chapter.

CHAPTER TWO

Scientific Method

A FORMER Master of Marlborough College in England recently described the opening sentence of a schoolboy essay on Science and Religion.[1] He had written : " The difference between Science and Religion is that Science is material and Religion is immaterial." This is an interesting sentence, reflecting a good deal of what is commonly felt about the mutual relationship of these two movements of the spirit. It is widely held, for example, that science is concerned with what is physical, religion with what is spiritual (and, of course, with nothing else!). Science deals with things that you can get hold of, and usually measure in a quantitative fashion; religion with things that you cannot get hold of, far less measure. It may be claimed that the things which are seen are temporal, and the things which are not seen are eternal. But since seeing is believing, the obvious corollary of all this is that science is relevant, religion is irrelevant; science matters, religion does not.

These widely held convictions will prove a good starting point for our present discussion. For in the last chapter I showed how there was a sense in which the development of science had rendered God obsolete. Made, as Voltaire would say, in our image, He could remain alive and active only so long as we were ignorant of true facts: the development of science would chase Him unceremoniously away. As Dr. J. Bronowski has put it:[2] the fundamental assumption "amounts to this, that science is to get rid of angels, blue fairies with red noses and other agents whose intervention would reduce the explanation of physical events to other than physical terms." There is no hope for a religious belief which either clings despairingly to the past, or digs its heels hard into the ground in defence of some hedgehog position, or searches out some unappropriated territory in which a "God of the Gaps" could be installed. We must seek some alternative mode of thought, and it must be one that will do justice to the splendour, the power, and the dynamic and progressive character of science.

There seems to me to be only one way out of our dilemma. If we cannot bring God in at the end of science, He must be there at the very start, and right through it. We have done wrong to set up any sharp antithesis between science and religion. Science itself must be a religious activity: "a fit subject for a Sabbath day's study," as John Ray put it in the seventeenth century. There is no other way out of our impasse than to assert that science is one aspect of God's presence, and scientists therefore part of the company of His heralds. In our earlier discussion we were arguing on wholly false premises; for we spoke as if we had somehow to discover a Paradise Regained, which should make a happy ending for the chapter of Paradise Lost. Now if science had really been the devil, the force of darkness, this might have been a fair account. But the case I want to make is quite different. I want to be able to look at science, its methods, its presuppositions, its basis, its splendid successes and its austere discipline; and then I want to be able to say: Here is God revealing Himself for those with eyes to see. If we can make that case then we can understand how so many scientists have been, and still are, Christians; and all this is possible without what would otherwise be an unbearable dichotomy of experience. Once we have established this situation we shall not need to waste our time and our effort in the fruitless controversies and futile arguments of the last chapter: we can open our minds to accept what science brings. At its deepest level the conflict becomes what Max Planck[3] called a " phantom problem," and our whole discussion is lifted to another plane of thought. There is still plenty to do, in resolving the tensions which are inevitable so long as science needs to progress and religious experience is clouded by human sin. But at least we see that the way is clear, and we can recognise the main lines along which we must travel.

All this follows from my chief thesis: and so we must turn ourselves to its elaboration. I propose to show that science is an essentially religious activity, and shall do so by trying to answer two questions: first, What is science trying to do? What does it mean by truth? and then, What presuppositions, or attitudes, are involved in the practice of science as we know it in the West? In both of these questions we shall see that profound changes have taken place in our thinking during the last fifty years, so that both questions must be answered differently now from then.

Let us begin with the first question: What is

science trying to do, and what is the nature of scientific truth? The old answer would have been quite simple: our task is to find out about the world, to see what it is like, to discover nature's laws and thereby to be able to control it. In Leibniz' phrase we set ourselves to solve Nature's cryptogram: and meanwhile, Nature herself looks on, impassively, yielding up her secrets as our search progresses. As for ourselves, in order to play our part, we must try to depersonalise ourselves so that we may the more effectively deal with an objective world, and be as nearly as possible uninfluenced and unimpeded by any prior view of what we ought, or would like, to find.

In almost every detail that answer is now superseded. For we have learnt that the things we thought we were describing do not have the properties we thought they had. In that enormous liberating revolution of the first twenty-five years of physics in this century, we came to realise that the very foundations of our subject were being removed from us. Physics had been built on the concept of mass and velocity, whose study is mechanics; and on the concept of an aether and its electric forces, whose study is electrodynamics; and on the concept of continuity of measurement, so that it should be possible in principle to trace the gradual changes which come over any system or systems, and so illustrate the law of cause and effect. Stage by stage every one of these convictions has been stripped off us. Einstein's relativity showed us that there was no such thing as an absolute position, or an absolute velocity: and that the same body would not appear to have the same mass to two observers who were travelling at different speeds relative to it. The experiments of Michelson and Morley showed us that there was no substantial aether through which our solar system travelled, and that electric and magnetic forces depended on how the experimenter moved. Heisenberg's famous Uncertainty Principle underlined what every psychologist knew in his heart, even if he was not very clever at expressing it in words: that no one person could ever exactly repeat the same experiment, nor could two different people ever make exactly the same measurement. Indeed, as the anatomists were showing,[4] all our brains, though constructed on the same general pattern, were different in detail, so that every one of us was bound to see things differently from his neighbour, and no truth could be exactly the same for any two people. One reason why no measurement could be repeated, with exactly identical results, was that the act of measurement, whether in psychology or physics, altered the system measured. The observer was not, and could never hope to be, independent of the thing that he observed. To ask a question of nature was to affect her, to change her, by however little: there was no prospect of ever recording a continuity of motion of any fundamental particle. Even the principle of cause and effect must be seen in statistical terms. As for the electron, that central figure in all modern physics, whose behaviour underlies the wireless set and all the complicated intricacies of the telephone exchange and the modern electronic computer, it cannot even be seen. The

naked eye, so sensitive that it can respond to a total
of no more than six quanta of light, will almost certainly never be able to see an electron—certainly it
has not done so yet. We have moved a long way
from Democritus : "nothing exists except atoms and
empty space; everything else is opinion." For we
admit unashamedly that the atom is a fiction of our
own mind; and as for space, it is at our choice
whether we call it straight or curved. All that happens if we reverse our choice is that the equations of
motion for an atom or a star become correspondingly
more complicated or more simple.

At first it may seem from all this that science has
been torpedoed, and scientific truth become a chi-
mera. But that is not true. We have come to see
the scientific implications of some of those things
which Kant had said in the eighteenth century; that
the raw material of science is the set of experiences,
observations, measurements, of the scientist; and his
task is to find a pattern of relationships between these
experiences. Science grows precisely in so far as the
pattern of relationships is seen to extend its range :
if the pattern cannot be extended, it soon ossifies and
is replaced by some new and more comprehensive
alternative : this is because scientists cannot bear to
live with a closed subject, and instinctively demand
an open one.

It may help to see this rationale of science if I
illustrate it with a very familiar example—the law of
universal gravitation. According to popular tradition
—unfortunately almost certainly untrue—Galileo
dropped various articles, such as stones of different

sizes and shapes, from the leaning tower of Pisa, and found that they all took roughly the same length of time to reach the ground. This is the beginning of the pattern, since size and shape are seen not to be significant. But later Newton in his orchard at Woolsthorpe in 1666 at the time of the Great Plague —and this story seems now as if it were substantially correct[5]—watches an apple fall, and realises that the law of falling bodies covers apples and stones, tall towers and small ones : and is the same in Lincolnshire as in Italy. The pattern begins to grow. Shortly afterwards he sees that the motion of the moon round the earth can be explained in the same way. The pattern develops. Next the orbits of the planets round the sun and the swinging of the candelabra of lights in church; these all fit in to the pattern. It becomes possible to use a small apparent misfit of the planet Uranus to predict the existence of a new planet Neptune—and in a different field altogether we believe so strongly in the truth of this pattern that we use it both to see whether or not the continents are floating, and also to prospect for oil.

This example shows us how the scientist works— striving continually to find a pattern of relationships that will " make sense," and on to which he can progressively graft new experiences, new observations. If the law which he has devised does not describe the experiences well enough, if it does not fit some new set of experiences, then he changes it; as when Einstein, reflecting on the way in which Newton's magnificent law of gravitation, however excellent it might be for laboratory experiments, yet could not deal with the recession of the distant galaxies, introduced a cosmical repulsion term into the expression of the law; or as when Gamov, in his effort to understand the emission of an alpha particle from a radioactive nucleus, " altered " the law of electrical attraction at sufficiently small distances.

Here we begin to see something about scientific law which was not sufficiently recognised till recently —that it is essentially a description of the results of observations. A scientific law does not control events : otherwise we could not alter it ourselves when we were dissatisfied with it. It is a means of correlating experiences. And the pattern to which it refers is a pattern built round concepts. There is no force of gravitation except in our own minds as they try to comprehend the falling stone; there is no electron except in our imagination as we seek to understand the behaviour of a wireless valve; there is no radioactive nucleus unless it be a creature of our own invention, conceived and born that we may the better make sense of flashes of light on a fluorescent screen, or the falling together of the leaves of an electroscope. What is important in science is that it grows by the progressive building of what J. B. Conant[6] has called grand conceptual schemes. These are the great patterns of science, within which there fit together the smaller patterns. As for these patterns, they are mental constructs of our own, and their ultimate sanction is that they do fit together. Scientific truth means coherence in a pattern which is recognised as meaningful and sensible. It is acceptable only so long as it does " hold together," without internal contradiction, and is able to grow, either by the prediction of new phenomena or the absorption of old ones. We could perfectly well use Kant's own words to describe all this : " Our intellect does not draw its laws from nature, but imposes its laws upon nature."

Truth, as I have said, lies in the pattern. We can see this very easily if we consider the situation in modern physics. This has become a very esoteric study, with its imposing list of candidates for the rank of fundamental particles. There are electrons, and neutrons, protons and positrons, positive, negative and neutral mesons,[7] light and heavy mesons, κ-mesons, χ-mesons, σ-particles and υ-particles. No one has seen, or touched, or smelt, or heard, any of them. The evidence that any one of them exists is bound up with the evidence for all of them. It would be almost impossible to reject any of this formidable crew without at the same time rejecting all. The strength of this pattern, as it is also the strength of the pattern of gravitation, lies in the interlocking character of its elements. Here is something that merits the term " discipline," for it is austere and comprehensive and whole. In the light of this account, it is amusing to recall some words of Michael Faraday, in a paper on electrochemistry which he read before the Royal Society in January, 1834 : " I must confess that I am jealous of the term atom, for though it is easy to talk of atoms, it is very difficult to form a clear idea of their nature." Out of the greater wisdom of a further hundred years of study of these atoms, we may still sometimes be tempted to

wonder whether they really exist at all. Yet we dare
not reject them; for they are our children, the fruit
of our minds.

This insistence on concepts and the way in which
their pattern mediates truth to us, should remind us
that we have now brought science much closer to
other disciplines than it has often been supposed to
be. Every true discipline of the mind shares this
common search for unifying concepts. The historian
seeks for pattern in the unending cycle of events just
as much as the psychologist or the artist. In a university it should hardly be necessary to labour this
point. It is the pattern that we value. The facts,
which are the raw material of the pattern, yet do not
belong to it; they are of relatively little value by
themselves. Only the pattern gives insight. Here is a
modern writer, not by any means a scientist, saying
how the search for pattern, however difficult, however obscure, is at rock bottom the search for satis-
faction and fulfilment:[8]

I think I have said enough to suggest that our
time is one in which it is quite impossible to detect
any one underlying pattern, or even any opposed
groups of underlying patterns. . . . Is it not possible, then, that one day, when nearly all our contemporaries have relapsed into a decent obscurity
for ever, a few simple facts will emerge as the only
significant ones? I doubt to-day if anyone can
foresee which they will be. But they will be connected with the search, along a dozen parallel
lines, for some principle of order in the affairs of
men. . . . The nearer you get to that principle of

order, the nearer you get to what I have called the Good Life.

When we recognise how it is in the concepts that the glory of each discipline lies, and not the bare facts on which these concepts rest, we can begin to see how strangely reversed in his judgment the school-boy of our opening sentences must have been. For it is not hard to show how, in at least one of its aspects, religion runs entirely parallel to this account of science. Thus there is a pattern here: a pattern whose detail may not be susceptible of independent proof any more than can that of the π meson: but a pattern which we can believe because it all holds together. Here, for example, is Martin Luther, in 1556, in his *Commentary on the Book of Daniel*, giving us his definition of God—or perhaps it would be more accurate to say, his test of what is a real and true conception of God:[9]

A God is simply that whereon the human heart rests with trust, faith, hope and love. If the resting is right, then the God is right; if the resting is wrong, then the God, too, is illusory.

As we shall see in a later chapter, there is more than this to say about belief in God. But a scientist could scarcely have put his grounds for belief in science any better. So also Kant, carrying what he called the new Copernican revolution into the field of religion, argues in a similar vein:[10]

Much as my words may startle you, you must not

condemn me for saying: every man creates his
God. From the moral point of view . . . you have
to create your God, in order to worship in Him
your creator. For in whatever way . . . the Deity
should be made known to you—even . . . if He
should reveal Himself to you: it is you . . . who
must judge whether you are permitted (by your
conscience) to believe in Him, and to worship
Him.

What is coming out of all this is a new relationship
to facts—a relationship which, because it is common
to so many and diverse disciplines—is certainly most
impressive. It is becoming clear that, whether in
science or history or religious experience, facts are
never known fully and can never be completely correlated. As a result our models—in science, the
atoms, the genes, the complexes and repressions of
the mind: in religion, the nature of God and His
mode of working in the world—can never be wholly
satisfactory. For at very least they must suffer from
one of two complaints. Either they are overdefined,
leading to internal inconsistency and contradiction;
or they are underdefined, leading to "fuzziness"
and imprecision. This is true both in science and in
religion; a moment's reflection will soon show us the
many evils that have resulted from trying to define
God too closely. Here is the besetting sin of the man
who is complacent and smug, just as much as of the
extreme fundamentalist. Did not Xenophon, 2,500
years ago, conclude:

There never has been, and never will be, a man

who has certain knowledge of the Gods, and about all the things I speak of. For even if he should happen to speak the truth, yet he himself does not know it.

Religion and science share here a common ignorance, and a common hope. Practically all Christians (though, alas, many non-Christians do not believe this, or are unwilling to admit it) know that religion is not merely facts. Facts there certainly are, for the Christian faith has its roots firmly fixed in a moment of history two thousand years ago. But the mature Christian faith has a greater growth superimposed, the relating of these facts in a meaningful coherent pattern. Precisely the same is true of science, and he who stops at the facts misses the glory. Sir Richard Gregory, the editor of *Nature,* from whom I quoted in the last chapter, spoke very feelingly of this:

> "Science," he said, "is not to be regarded merely as a storehouse of facts to be used for material purposes, but as one of the great human endeavours to be ranked with arts and religion as the guide and expression of man's fearless quest for truth."

So we see that there is much that is common in the approach of science and religion to the treatment of facts. Without doubt, as I said before, the facts are there; for people make measurements and record their findings; they dream dreams and write poetry; they think thoughts and record history. But in all these the facts are secondary, and what used to be

called "objective facts" are beginning to fade away.
Indeed, our claim to any sort of final truth is a pre-
posterous conceit that we must ridicule. "The history of human kind," says Professor Heller,[11] "is a
repository of scuttled objective truths. All relevant
'objective truths' are born and die as absurdities.
They come into being as the monstrous claim of the
inspired rebel, and pass away with the eccentricity of
a superstitious crank." No one who looks honestly at
the story either of science or religion will fail to recognise both the inspiration and the superstition. But
that is no reason for rejecting either science or religion : nor for expecting from the one a kind of proof
not vouchsafed by the other. It was a cardinal of
the Church, none other than John Henry Newman,
who could write in his Grammar of Assent that we
reach certainties, not through logic, but by some
sort of intuitive perception, building up from "the
cumulation of probabilities," each of which is "too
fine to avail separately, too subtle and circuitous to
be convertible into syllogisms," a living awareness of
truth. Thus, although there will always be a wide
measure of common belief in the fields both of
science and of religion, there will always be a border
country in both, where what is true for one person
may not have the same compelling power over another. As Newman himself said : "It follows that
what to one intellect is a proof is not so to another,
and that the certainty of a proposition does properly
consist in the certitude of the mind that contemplates
it." The forward and dynamic character of science
could hardly have been better described.

We have just seen how, though facts are the raw

material of science, they do not constitute its glory.
Lord Rutherford was accustomed to refer to those
scientists who were content to gather facts as "stamp-
collectors," though I believe this term would be
counted much too generous by any serious phila-
telist! Yet it is strange how often even great scientists
misunderstand their own work in this respect. What
could be more false than Isaac Newton at the end of
his life describing himself as "picking up pebbles"
on the great beach of knowledge; or than Charles
Darwin writing of himself that "my mind seems to
have become a kind of machine for grinding general
laws out of large collections of facts"? For Newton
himself said that "no great discovery is ever made
without a bold guess," and Darwin's magnificent
contribution to science is still referred to as the *theory*
of evolution, by the very manner of whose wording
we recognise the intrusion of imagination and inspiration, passing beyond mere facts. Professor Bever-
idge[12] at Cambridge has recently gathered together
several comments on this situation, made by the
scientists themselves. They show how greatness in
science is associated not with facts, but with imagination. I will quote but two. First there is T. H.
Huxley: "It is a popular delusion that the scientific
enquirer is under an obligation not to go beyond
generalisation of observed facts . . . but anyone who
is practically acquainted with scientific work is aware
that those who refuse to go beyond the facts, rarely
get so far." And then there is Pasteur: "If someone
tells me that in making these conclusions I have gone
beyond the facts, I reply: 'It is true that I have
freely put myself among ideas which cannot be rigor-

ously proved. That is my way of looking at things.' "
"Wise men," said Professor G. Temple, "do not
believe in either facts or theories; they accept facts
and they use theories."

Linked closely with this is an element of doubt. It
is almost as if before one jumped, one had to shut
one's eyes : or as if, before a new creative idea could
come, the mind had to be almost broken. Perhaps
it could be called a sense of humility before the incompleteness of one's knowledge. And certainly this
feeling has always been a constant companion with
the great scientists. In his *Dialogue on the Great
World Systems* Galileo Galilei wrote these words :

> I always accounted as extraordinarily foolish those
> who would make human comprehension the mea-
> sure of what Nature has a power or knowledge to
> effect, whereas on the contrary there is not any
> least effect in Nature which can be fully under-
> stood by the most speculative minds in the world.
> Their vain presumption of knowing all can take
> beginning solely from their never having known
> anything, for if one has but once experienced the
> perfect knowledge of one thing, and truly tasted
> what it is to know, he shall perceive that of infinite
> other conclusions he understands not so much as
> one.

Galileo died in 1642. But his principle remains the
same. John Ray, [13] a little later, can say of his biological studies :

> If I am to be quite honest, there are many points

on these subjects still open to doubt; questions can be raised which I confess I am not competent to solve or to disentangle; this is not because they have not got definite natural explanations, but because I am ignorant of them.

I seem to hear an echo of some other cry: "Lord, I believe; help Thou mine unbelief." It is as if science was only possible to those who could doubt. Newton[14] could say "the cause of gravity is what I do not pretend to know"; Descartes could add that "in order to reach the Truth, it is necessary once in one's life to put everything in doubt—as far as possible"; and more recently the anatomist Professor J. Z. Young[15] labelled his Reith lectures for 1950: *Doubt and Certainty in Science*. It was in the same year that the physicist Professor J. R. Oppenheimer wrote of the relation of scientific research to the liberal university as follows:

It is a world in which inquiry is sacred, and freedom of inquiry is sacred. It is a world in which doubt is not only a permissible thing, but in which doubt is the indispensable method of aiming at truth. It is a world in which the notion of novelty, of hitherto unexpected experience, is always with us and in which it is met by open-mindedness that comes from having known, of having seen over and over again that one had a great deal to learn. . . . The nature of the discipline of science is its devotion, its dedication to finding out when you are wrong, to the detection of error.

No one who reads that quotation with an open mind can possibly fail to see how the central character of doubt, of humility and of freedom of enquiry which is "sacred," require the intrusion of things conventionally described as spiritual. If these words have any meaning, then science must not be denied some spiritual content. But more of that later.

Linked with the acceptance of doubt there comes the rejection of unnecessary authority. Science has its High Priests, and they hold their office because of the creative work that they have done. They may—and usually do—deserve their authority, but the greatest advances have come when that authority has been rejected. This is one reason why most really brilliant scientific discoveries are made by young men.[16] No one has stated this better than T. H. Huxley:

> The improver of natural knowledge absolutely refuses to acknowledge authority as such. For him scepticism is the highest of duties; blind faith the unpardonable sin. And it cannot be otherwise, for every great advance in natural knowledge has involved the absolute rejection of authority, the cherishing of the keenest scepticism, the annihilation of the spirit of blind faith.

Christian believers all the way from Martin Luther, nailing his theses to the Church doorway, right down to the humblest Christian who can sing Charles Wesley's hymn: "My God, I know, I feel Thee mine," are aware that it is out of the rejection of authority of others that the sense of personal release has come.

He who has never been lost has almost certainly never been found.

The relationship of truth to a pattern means that truth, including scientific truth, must ultimately be thought of as a whole, and not as " a bit here and a bit there." What Whitehead said, long ago now, is perfectly correct : " The notion of the complete self-sufficiency of any item of finite knowledge is the fundamental error of dogmatism. Every such item derives its truth, and its very meaning, from its un-analysed relevance to the background which is the unbounded universe. . . . Every scrap of our knowledge derives its meaning from the fact that we are factors in the universe, and are dependent on the universe for every detail of our existence." This concept of truth as something whole, something related, is to be found almost everywhere. For example, in the latest translation of the four Gospels, by E. V. Rieu,[17] he talks about the Gospel of St. Luke. " I do not mean," he says in the preface, " when I say Luke is a poet, that he has embroidered his narratives, but rather that he knew how to distil truth from fact." This illustrates that what I have been saying about science holds exactly in other fields.

But the pattern develops and grows. Truth, we may say, itself develops and grows; it is not and cannot be static. It is most dangerous to speak of " the truth once and for all delivered," of whatever kind that truth may be. It is one of the most interesting and curious things about the passion for truth which the scientist exhibits (and I believe this would be true for other types of people also) that he recognises this developing character and even looks for it. The

Oxford University Press tell me that if a new scientific textbook requires no alteration for five years, they are satisfied. After that it is almost sure to need correction. And this is what Faraday says in the preface to his *Experimental Researches in Electricity* :

> Although I cannot honestly say that I *wish* to be found in error, yet I do fervently hope that the progress of science in the hands of the many zealous cultivators will be such as, by giving us new and other developments, and laws more and more general in their applications, will make even me think that what is written and illustrated in these experimental researches, belongs to the by-gone parts of science.

When we read words like these we can scarcely help feeling that we are getting to the heart and understanding of scientific truths. That which I own as true and have discovered by myself is only a little element, or contribution, which must play its part and be built into the bigger scheme. It is in this way that scientific truth is so closely associated with growth and vitality and life.

There is one aspect of this progressive pattern of science which is important because it differentiates it from many of the other patterns of interpretation. We can see this best if we ask how modern science began. What was the change of outlook which, beginning in the thirteenth century but growing fast in the sixteenth and seventeenth centuries, fostered the development of the scientific method? We can answer this question in several ways, all of them essentially equivalent. One of these was the recognition that cause and effect was a relationship which could be studied in a small way, without endeavouring the impossible task of Aristotelian physics, wherein everything is related to Final Causes. No longer do we say: " iron sinks in water and cork floats because they are each seeking their proper place, or are obedient to the potency within them." Rather do we say: " iron sinks and cork floats because there is a simple property associated with all iron and all cork—their density; if this exceeds the density of water the substance sinks: otherwise it floats." But how the density ever comes to have its particular value, is a problem that we do not even try to solve. " I scruple not, ' wrote Newton, " to propose the Principles of Motion above-mentioned, they being of very general extent, and leave their causes to be found out."[18] So also Bacon:

The introduction of such (i.e. Final) causes into physics has displaced and driven out the investigation of physical causes, making men rest in specious and shadowy causes . . . to the great detriment of science. And this I find to be true not only of Plato, but also of Aristotle, Galen and many others who frequently sail upon the same shallows.

All this does not mean, as John Baillie[19] has pointed out, that there are no Final Causes, but only that natural science has yet no business with them: they are not yet discoverable by empirical methods. And, as Bacon goes on to say: this treatment of causes does not cast any doubt on the providential ordering of nature; rather does it exalt it.

An alternative way of describing this is to say that we have decided to ask easy questions where progress may be expected; rather than hard ones, where its chance is at best minute. When Galileo started to experiment with balls on inclined planes, it must have seemed to many of his contemporaries that he was missing the mark. How much more exciting to speculate on the Final Causes, the ultimate realities, the mysteries of life and death, than to seek a little formula for an uninteresting physical event. Yet that was the way that science grew: the pattern began in a very modest way. Whitehead has drawn our attention to the change that came over science when people decided to leave these great issues, and choose smaller ones which they could "pin-point," and on to which they could bring to bear all the mental armoury that they had. And Dingle[20] has told us that

we need to cultivate the restraint of Galileo, who left the world of angels and spirits until the time should come when it could be explored, and contented himself with such principles as he could extract with confidence from experience, though the resolution committed him to such trivialities as the timing of balls rolling down grooves. It is that self-control—the voluntary restriction to the task of extending knowledge outwards from the observed to the unobserved instead of imposing imagined universal principles inwards on the world of observation—that is the essential hallmark of the man of science, distinguishing him most fundamentally from the non-scientific philosopher.

We too had better leave the world of angels and spirits until the time comes—if indeed it ever does come along this direction of progress—when we are ready and able to deal with it. In many things we shall do well to follow Galileo's recommendation to his readers " to pronounce that wise, ingenious and modest sentence, ' I do not know.' "

It is at this stage that we begin to see the distinctive character that separates science from other disciplines, such as art. In both, truth is not just the acquisition of fact, or increase of knowledge. In both, it is a relationship between ourselves and some reality, which we express and translate in terms of pattern. But while the scientist seeks for some law within which the particular is lost in the general, the artist is pre-eminently concerned with the particular aspect of some general relationship : for him it is *this* tree, *this* mountain, *this* face, which expresses truth. So when van Gogh paints a chestnut tree, it is this *particular* chestnut tree and no other, which has significance. " Art," said Whistler, " since it begins with the infinite, cannot progress." And Beethoven said of music, that " it is a higher revelation than all wisdom and philosophy."

I have just been speaking of one sense in which science differs from other ways of knowing. But it is important to recognise in how many more ways it resembles them. First I shall put the use of the imagination. We have already seen that facts themselves are of little importance, as compared with the interpretation we put upon them. But that interpretation is a creative art. It was Max Planck[21] who said that "science was a created work of art," because :

> when the pioneer in science sends forth the groping feelers of his thoughts, he must have a vivid intuitive imagination, for new ideas are not generated by deduction, but by an artistically creative imagination.

And Bronowski[22] can say that "the layman's key to science is its unity with the arts." How disastrously unfortunate it is for the proper understanding of science that it has so frequently been described as if it were dull deduction from observed facts in the manner suggested by Francis Bacon's Novum Organum, when, all the time, practically every advance in science has been the result of a mental leap; and when, even in mathematics, we detect a strain sometimes of austere beauty, and at other times of romantic thrill. My colleague Professor Temple could choose as the title of his recent Inaugural Lecture at Oxford : *The Classical and Romantic in Natural Philosophy*. And Sir William Rowan Hamilton, Astronomer Royal of Ireland and himself a distinguished mathematician, could call the French mathematical physicist Lagrange the "Shakespeare of Mathematics," on account of the extraordinary beauty, elegance and depth of the Lagrangian methods. The author of a recent text-book on dynamics[23] says in his preface how " again and again the author experienced the extraordinary elation of mind which accompanies a preoccupation with the basic principles and methods of analytical mechanics." But perhaps the clearest expression of this is in an unpublished article written by the late N. R. Campbell:[24] he tells of how, on one day in 1913, a copy of the *Philosophical Magazine* fell out of his bookcase and lay open on the floor:

> Some algebraic formulae caught my eye . . . it was part of a paper by a Mr. N. Bohr, of whom I had never heard. . . . I sat down and began to read. In half an hour I was in a state of excitement and ecstasy, such as I have never experienced before or since in my scientific career. I had just finished a year's work revising a book on Modern Electrical Theory. These few pages made everything I had written entirely obsolete. That was a little annoying, no doubt. But the annoyance was nothing to the thrill of a new revelation, such as must have inspired Keats' most famous sonnet. And I had so nearly missed the joy of discovering this work for myself, and rushing up to the laboratory to be the first to tell everyone else about it . . . twenty years have not damped my enthusiasm.

This is very startling, but it is by no means unique. Another distinguished professor of mathematics in Britain said in a public lecture not so long ago : " we can test out theories by this; are they beautiful ?" And here is the judgment on a man, Victor Goldsmidt, who penetrated to the inner secrets of crystal structure: "In a few years' time, Goldsmidt's work . . . will take a place beside, if it does not replace, the work of Lavoisier, in the merit of not being merely true, but also extremely simple and beautiful."

This is how science becomes an adventure—an adventure of the mind, in which beauty, elegance and thrill link it with wider experience, and the feeling of mankind in many diverse ways. This is so important that I must illustrate it once again: and I will choose some words from a passage at the end of an address by Sir Cyril Hinshelwood which he gave at the recent Centenary Celebrations of the Chemical Society of London:[25] he speaks of chemistry, but its spirit applies to all science:

And now to the conclusion of the whole matter. What the Society is and must continue above all else to be is a fellowship of those who share the love of chemistry, that most excellent child of intellect and art. Chemistry provides not only a mental discipline, but an adventure and an aesthetic experience. Its followers seek to know the hidden causes which underlie the transformations of our changing world, to learn the essence of the rose's colour, the lilac's fragrance, and the oak's tenacity, and to understand the secret paths by which the sunlight and the air create these wonders.

And to this knowledge they attack an absolute value, that of truth and beauty. The vision of Nature yields the secret of power and wealth, and for this it may be sought by many. But it is revealed only to those who seek it for itself. Its pursuit has united the predecessors whom we commemorate: it will unite our successors for as long as the spirit of man endures.

Some of the implications of this moving passage will become clear later. But, even now, there can be no denying that it ranges science with the arts.

There is more to be said, however, about this relationship. Both science, art, history and religion are profoundly subject to, and influenced by, the thought-forms of their age. This conclusion follows simply enough, once we have admitted the rôle of the imagination, and the sense of progress, which these all involve. For neither in science, nor in art, can we divest ourselves of the mental climate in which we live. Perhaps this is why the great ages of science have so often been contemporaneous with the great ages of the arts,[26] despite the wide misconception that science destroys culture. In ancient Greece Socrates taught in the hey-day of the Greek drama: Leonardo da Vinci was a painter, a sculptor, a mathematician and an engineer; the first table of logarithms was published within a few years of Shakespeare's First Folio; the Royal Society received its name from one of its most enthusiastic members, John Evelyn the diarist. In this relationship to its environment, science and art are one with history. R. G. Collingwood suggests that "what particular parts or aspects of the past we now recall by historical thought, depends on our present interests and attitudes towards life." And J. T. Shotwell[27] tells us that "the interpretations of history are but the reflex of the local environment, the expression of the dominant interest of the time." This is well enough known for history and art, but not so well known for science. Yet it is just as much true. Kepler, in studying the motions of the planets, could be moved to an ecstasy of delight that they seemed to describe such perfect circles; and in doing so he was responding to the sense of purity of form derived from the Greeks. So also a modern biologist[28] draws attention to the way in which, almost simultaneously, similar ideas about Nature appear all over the world :

> The future historian of our times will note as a remarkable phenomenon that since the time of the First World War, similar conceptions about Nature, mind, life and society, arose independently, not only in different sciences, but also in different countries. Everywhere we find the same leading motifs : concepts of organisation showing new characteristics and laws at each level, those of the dynamic nature of reality and the antitheses within it.

It is not difficult to see the underlying reason for this : science, no less than art, history and religion, is bound up with men, their habits, customs, values, thought-forms and traditions. The significance of this common coherence will appear in chapter 3, when we consider the rôle of the person. For the present it will be sufficient to recognise that science may not properly be isolated, since it shares with these other disciplines so large a common quality. Two or three years ago, I read a most interesting account of the book *Male and Female,* by Margaret Mead. The reviewer referred to an appendix where Dr. Mead discussed the function of the social scientist. Then, very wisely as it seems to me, he added: " The author faces these problems, but she does not solve them. The social scientist is, after all, a product of the society to which he or she belongs, and one asks whether Dr. Mead is not herself a symptom of a changing attitude towards the problems with which she deals." Many of us would want to say just the same about the later work of Dr. Kinsey.

Our discussion has already moved towards an answer to the second of the main questions with which we began this chapter: what presuppositions, or attitudes, are involved in the practice of science, as we know it in the West? Here, as in our earlier question about what science tries to do, we shall find that the answer has been profoundly modified in the last fifty years. This does not mean that scientists have altered their way of doing science, but merely that they have considered rather more carefully just what they do and how they set about doing it. In the older view, once Aristotelian and Thomistic metaphysics had been abandoned, no presuppositions remained. Man would see what he would see, discover what he would discover, without any prior influence or emotive element in his approach. We have to thank people like A. N. Whitehead and M. Polanyi for revising that answer now. In his famous Riddell Lectures of 1946 on *Science, Faith and Society*[29] Polanyi has these opening words:

I shall re-examine here the suppositions underlying our belief in science, and propose to show that they are more extensive than is usually thought. They will appear to co-extend with the entire spiritual foundations of man, and to go to the very root of his social existence. Hence, I will urge, our belief in science should be regarded as a token of much wider convictions.

It is nothing less than tragic that this is so widely misunderstood. The greater part of our schoolboy's acceptance of science and rejection of religion springs from his unexamined belief that science accepts no presuppositions, and must therefore be superior to a Christianity which is overloaded with them. Yet this view is wholly wrong. Theodor Mommsen's famous phrase " science without presuppositions " is a hopelessly superficial description of our discipline. Think for a moment of some of the attitudes of mind with which any scientist comes to his search : there is honesty, and integrity, and hope : there is enthusiasm, for no one ever yet began an experiment without an element of passion : there is an identification of himself with the experiment, a partisan character about his secret hope for its conclusion which not even an adverse result can wholly extinguish : there is a humility before a created order of things, which are to be received and studied : there is a singleness of mind about the search which reveals what the scientist himself may often hesitate to confess, that he does what he does because it seems exciting and it somehow fulfils a deep part of his very being : there is co-operation with his fellows, both in the same laboratory, and across the seven seas: there is patience, akin to that which kept Mme. Curie at her self-imposed task of purifying eight tons of pitchblende to extract the few odd milligrams of radium: above all there is judgment—judgment as to what constitutes worthwhile research: judgment as to what is fit and suitable for publication. No wonder that a modern scientist—and no Christian either—has to say that "science cannot exist without judgments of value."

Indeed this is the case: science could not exist, and certainly is not practised, without all these qualities. They build the ethos and the tradition which every scientist must accept and to which he must conform. One could illustrate them in a thousand ways—the physiologist Pavlov writes his *Bequest to Academic Youth,* in which he asks the question: "What can I wish to the youth of my country who devote themselves to science?" and in which he concludes . . . "Thirdly, passion. Remember that science demands from a man all his life. If you had two lives that would not be enough for you. Be passionate in your work and in your searching." Or—in a different way—an international conference takes place: everyone has the same right to speak: no national barriers, except the difficulties of language, exist between the members: if they are brought in forcibly from outside for political or any other reasons, we are ashamed of them: and, oddly enough, when they meet together to gossip around the coffee table, scientists speak much more of what they cannot do, or have failed to achieve, than of those things in which they have been successful. What stands out most clearly, though it may never even be explicitly mentioned, is that there really is a common search, and it is a common search for a common truth.

This quality of mind belongs not only to the mathematical form of thought, but to the moral and ethical issues which are related. Not only do we believe that there *is* a truth, and that this truth is accessible to all people; but equally we know what is good or bad science, whether in experiment or theory, and we adopt towards our publication the highest conceivable standards of integrity; furthermore we expect the same of others. Any falling short of that code is regarded with the utmost seriousness. It is not only that the young doctor, who from the first moment that he subscribes to the Hippocratic oath, accepts some measure of responsibility for the welfare of all men everywhere, it is equally that those who are not medicals, but physicists, chemists, or biologists, claim to take responsibility both for the truth of what they publish and for the whole of their consequences, so far as they can be foreseen. We demand the right, as scientists, so far as the life of the community permits, to decide in what fields of work we shall study, and freely to consult others working in similar fields. It is being true to the genius of the scientific tradition which we sustain that we protest against being made the instruments of anyone else's policy. In words used a few years ago in the *Bulletin of the Atomic Scientists of Chicago,* we know that " the degradation of the position of the scientist as an independent worker and thinker to that of a morally irresponsible stooge in a science factory," is ruinous both to the morale of the scientist and the quality of his scientific output. Patience, humility, fair-mindedness, integrity, co-operation, these are the hall-marks of our tradition. And they force me to the conclusion that this tradition is ultimately based on, and derives its final sanction from, moral convictions which are often unrecognised, but none the less imperative.

If one tenth of what I have just been saying is correct then science is full of presuppositions—it is true that these may be derived from some earlier metaphysic, but they have been adopted and, like most presuppositions, their existence is frequently not recognised even by those most affected by them. In this case the presuppositions are such as to carry science, properly understood, into the realm of religion. For that common search for a common truth; that unexamined belief that facts are correlatable, i.e. stand in relation to one another and cohere in a scheme; that unprovable assumption that there is an "order and constancy in Nature," without which the patient effort of the scientist would be only so much incoherent babbling and his publication of it in a scientific journal for all to read pure hypocrisy; all of it is a legacy from religious conviction. No one has put this more finely than Whitehead, in his *Science and the Modern World*:

I do not think, however, that I have even yet brought out the greatest contribution of Mediaevalism to the formation of the scientific movement. I mean the inexpugnable belief that every detailed occurrence can be correlated with its antecedents in a perfectly definite manner exemplifying general principles. Without this belief the incredible labours of scientists would be without hope. It is this instinctive conviction, vividly poised before the imagination, which is the motive power of research —that there is a secret, a secret which can be revealed. How has this conviction been so vividly implanted in the European mind? When we compare this tone of thought in Europe with the attitude of other civilisations when left to themselves, there seems but one source for its origin. It must come from the medieval insistence on the rationality of God, conceived as with the personal energy of Jehovah and with the rationality of a Greek philosopher. Every detail was supervised and ordered : the search into nature could only result in the vindication of the faith in rationality.

This is so important that I must illustrate it. In a letter of Sir William Herschel to the astronomer Maskelyne, written in 1782, he describes the way in which he reasoned to the idea of a cosmological universe in every part of which characteristics would be displayed similar to those which we see and measure in the neighbourhood of our own solar system.[30]

When I say : " Let the stars be supposed *one with another* to be about the size of the sun," I only mean this in the same extensive signification in which we affirm that *one with another* men are of such and such a particular height. This does neither exclude the Dwarf, nor the Giant. An oak tree also is of a certain size, though it admits of great variety. And . . . we shall soon allow that by mentioning the size of Man, or of the oak tree, we speak not without some real limits. . . . If we see such conformity in the whole animal and vegetable kingdom that we can, without injury to truth, affix a certain Idea to the size of the species, it appears to me highly probable, and analogous to Nature, that the same regularity will hold good with regard to the fixt stars.

It was precisely because Herschel could argue like this that he made his fine discoveries, and earned his title of " the Father of Sidereal Astronomy."

It was just the same with Balmer, almost exactly a hundred years later, when he began to study the wavelengths of the different colours of light emitted in a discharge tube of hydrogen gas. It was his desire to reveal the " divine orderliness " in the universe that led him to the discovery of the spectral series that bears his name, and thereby opened up a wholly new field in physics.

But there are other matters closely connected with this. If there is no ultimate and final proof of any scientific theory that may be proposed, but only the possibility of disproof when a clear prediction is not fulfilled, how does a scientist assess the validity of his theories? What judgment does he bring to bear? What considerations does he consider adequate in establishing a theory, or in building up the grand conceptual scheme of which we spoke earlier? The answer to these questions reveals again that the scientific movement is sustained by presuppositions and conventions which lie outside strict science. To speak of the universality of a law as, for example, the law of gravitation; or of its coherence in a pattern, as with the various mesons to which we have already referred, does not exhaust our answer. For why do we have an instinctive feeling that scientific laws ought to be simple? Why do we assert so insistently the absolute necessity of Ockham's razor? Why do we respond to something in our science that cannot be described otherwise than as beauty? Crowds of examples can be adduced to show that in fact all these influences are allowed to work upon us. Thus Clerk Maxwell, to whom we owe the systematisation of electricity and magnetism, had on one occasion verified a certain law (Ohm's law) to an exceedingly high degree of accuracy. This gave rise to his famous comment :

> It is seldom, if ever, that so searching a test has been applied to a law which was originally established by experiment, and which must still be considered as a purely empirical law, as it has not hitherto been deduced from the fundamental principles of dynamics. But the mode in which it has borne this test not only warrants our entire reliance on its accuracy . . . but encourages us to believe that the simplicity of an empirical law may be an argument for its exactness.

If we may take another example to show how deeply this conviction of simplicity lies at the heart of the scientific method, we may choose the case of John

Robison, afterwards Professor of Natural Philosophy at Edinburgh University. Sir Edmund Whittaker[31] has pointed out that in 1769, by direct experiment, he obtained the result that the force of repulsion between two like electrical charges was proportional to the inverse 2.06th power of the distance between them. But in the theory which he subsequently adopted on the basis of these experiments, the force was held to be proportional to the inverse square of the distance. This latter formula was obtained as an idealisation of the former, suggested by a conviction that a law of nature must exhibit a simple mathematical form. It is not many years ago since, at a public lecture in Oxford, Einstein said that "our experience up to date justifies us in feeling that in nature is actualised the idea of mathematical simplicity." It is not surprising that despite long discussions with Whitehead he was unwilling to abandon his theory of relativity, "against which neither logical nor experimental reasons could be cited, nor considerations of simplicity and beauty." In the same month in which these words are being written two chemical crystallographers[32] discuss the shape of the molecule of benzene. After calculating the positions of the various atoms as well as their measurements permit, and drawing the best plane that can be drawn to pass near their positions, they determine the perpendicular distances of these atoms away from this plane. These values do not vanish, since the atoms do not exactly lie on the plane : but they are small. The authors conclude : this shows "that the molecule is accurately planar." Their use of the word "accurately" is entirely in keeping with the spirit of science : but it is very revealing.

I have dwelt at some length on these presuppositions because I believe that they help us to see the close links between science and religion. If what I have said is in any real sense true, then science is only possible in a community where certain religious views are widely held. We shall be prepared to agree with the late Archbishop Temple :

> It may be too much to argue, as some students of the subject have done, that science is a fruit of Christianity, but it may be safely asserted that it can never spontaneously grow up in regions where the ruling principle of the Universe is believed to be either capricious or hostile.

So also Einstein, in some words carved above the fireplace in a room at Fine Hall, Princeton : " God who creates and is nature, is very difficult to understand, but He is not arbitrary or malicious."

When we see things like this, we begin to see the fulfilment that a man finds in science—what Bishop Barnes of Birmingham called "a purifying influence" and a "true humanism." This fulfilment links him with his comrades in other fields of knowledge. It was actually a writer, Mr. Somerset Maugham, who wrote of his profession in these words :[34] " The only valid and sensible reason I know for adopting the profession of literature is that you have so strong and urgent a desire to write that you cannot resist it." But this sense of vocation, or " calling," applies equally to the scientist. As the great historian of science, George Sarton[35] puts it:

> It is true that most men of letters, and, I am sorry to add, not a few scientists, know science only by its material achievement, but ignore its spirit, and see neither its internal beauty nor the beauty it extracts from the bosom of nature . . . a true humanist must know the life of science as he knows the life of art and the life of religion.

Now that we have got so far as this, we are ready to consider again my opening claim. I asserted that, on the basis both of its actions and its search for truth, and of its mode of working and its presuppositions, science must be described as an essentially religious activity. However little its followers may recognise this, it is still true that science is " helping to put a face on God "; it is one of the ways in which He is revealed.

Where men waver about the value of reason, the growth of science is an insistent reminder of its worth, recalling us to worship the Lord our God with all our mind : when we are tempted to retreat from the world into a subjective shell, it comes to remind us of that relatedness to the actual real world most clearly shown in the incarnation of God in Christ; when we lean to a superior personal conceit and forget that all men are one family, it comes to us with its belief in universalism, which is derived from and is still expressed most fundamentally in the Christian ideal of the brotherhood of man; when we are timid and afraid in face of overweening authority, then its rugged individualism, wherein the leading of one's own thought and the dictates of one's own conscience and judgment are felt to be more important than those of organised authority, is a reminder of the worth of every separate soul; when we hesitate before the magnitude of evil and the oppressive weight of the things that need to be done, its belief in progress or meliorism, which is not necessarily of the inevitable evolutionary type, and which has its source in Christian perfectionism and Protestant activism, should spur us to action; when we think of the flowering of the human intellect in the humility, patience, imagination, one-ness and splendour of modern science; then we should agree[36] not only that "science is a moral enterprise," but that it holds within itself the very stuff of religious experience. And so, since the Order of Physical Nature is one aspect of God showing Himself to His children, what they see and do when they study it is most intimately bound up both with what He is, and what they are. The schoolboy who tried to separate science and religion was completely and utterly wrong : what he should have said was that science was one part of religion and the splendour, the power, the dynamic and progressive character of science are nothing but the splendour and the power and the dynamic character of God, progressively revealed to us. We do them justice as we honour Him. With such common features as these, it is entirely right that Max Planck[37] should end his *Scientific Autobiography* with these words :

Religion and natural science are fighting a joint battle in an incessant, never relaxing crusade against scepticism and against dogmatism, against disbelief and against superstition, and the rallying cry in this crusade has always been, and always will be: "On to God."

CHAPTER THREE

The Human Element

IN our first chapter I showed that if God is to be found in science at all, it must be as an absolutely integral part of it. There was no hope for any scheme which tried to fit Him in between the gaps left over after science had first claimed its possessions. In the next chapter I showed how this could be, since science was an essentially religious activity, characterised by much the same temper and spirit as religion. It was possible to make the claim that science was one aspect of the revelation of God. Our reasons for taking this stand were twofold. First there were the presuppositions underlying all scientific effort and often, though not always, unexamined by the scientist. These, when they were uncovered, were seen to involve a belief in the universal character of truth, in what our prayer book calls the " order and constancy of Nature," and the sense of spiritual fulfilment which accompanies the practice of science. We might have used some words of Einstein : " Most people say that it is the intellect which makes a great scientist. They are wrong : it is the character." Our second reason for asserting that science as a religious activity sprang out of a consideration of the way science works : how it is based on experiences which are to be fitted into a pattern that must satisfy us as

84

meaningful. Here it was clear that the human element must play a not inconsiderable part: indeed no rationale of science is possible which neglects or diminishes this element. The conceptual schemes, or patterns, which are the glory of science, are constructs of our own, into which we breathe the living spirit. It was J. J. Thomson, Master of my Cambridge College, Trinity, who said: "I take the view that a theory should be a policy and not a creed, that its most important work is to suggest things that can be tried by experiment."

In this chapter I propose to consider in more detail the rôle of the human element in these relationships. But first there is one corollary which follows from our claim that science is a mode of God's revelation. The experiences on which science is based are not just random events. They are related to each other, and are ultimately held together, by the fact that they are God's revelation. I want to say of them that every experience is an encounter—an encounter with some reality to which we can give no other name but God. In the next chapter we shall see the importance of this in terms of what we can rightly say about the nature of God from a study of science. But for the present let us realise that, as A. N. Whitehead has put it: "Every event on its finer side introduces God into the world."[1] This is true whatever the nature of the event—whether it be the mental aberrations of a Hitler, the poetic imagination of a Shakespeare or a Goethe, just as much as if it is the falling of a stone or the existence of a fossil. The psalmist is quite right: "The earth is the Lord's, and the fulness thereof; the world, and they that dwell therein."[2] As we have already seen, nothing less than this is in the least degree acceptable.

This leads us right into our immediate programme. If it is really true, as I have claimed, that science is a religious activity, why do not all scientists recognise this? Why are they not all professing Christians? May it be that there are alternative frames of reference within which our experiences may be seen to fit into a pattern? Are these alternative patterns all equally valid? And if so, what is their mutual relationship? This will require us to probe more deeply into the manner in which the human element is involved. We shall see that man-the-scientist plays a curious dual rôle; without the recognition of this, we cannot get the full understanding of our science, nor properly see either its power or its limitations. Let us deal with the problem of alternative modes of description first.

We can put our question like this. The experiences which form the raw material of science are encounters with some reality. But are they the only way in which that reality is mediated to us? And are there alternative representations of it in terms of different frames of description? I believe there are, and will illustrate my argument in terms of an analogy which I have found useful; though, like all analogies, it is not perfect.

A few years ago I was partly responsible for the construction of an underground laboratory. It was at King's College, London University, and its rather curious location, directly underneath the main College quadrangle, was forced upon us by the exigencies of space in central London. While the laboratory was in course of construction, we had frequent occasion to consult the architect, and look through the large sheaf of drawings that he had in his office. Some of these were plans, showing us what the floor space would look like to an imaginary observer overhead : others were elevations, from one side or one end; or they were sections, in different directions and at different levels. Many of the diagrams looked utterly unlike the others : some showed features not present in the rest. Occasionally there were substantial common elements as when a plan and an elevation showed the existence of a boundary wall. Some drawings, from their very nature, showed a lot of detail; others showed relatively little; but, so far as the architect could make them, each was complete. None of them was exhaustive, and it would always be possible to imagine additional drawings, as for example sections in a different direction, which would resemble existing drawings in greater or less degree, though they would not be identical with any.

Now despite all these differences, we know perfectly well that there is only one building. These are representations of it, in the form appropriate to a piece of paper which is only two-dimensional. We need to have several of these drawings before we can say that we know what the building is really like. From one point of view, not a single one among all these drawings is ultimately redundant; and every drawing will have something particular to tell us about the building. To the uninitiated, it will seem almost impossible that all of these several descriptions can be "true," though in fact they are; or that they represent one building, as in fact they do.

This is the analogy. Its application to our problem is quite obvious. For the building stands for the reality God, who is being described in the separate disciplines (or diagrams). The modes of description vary greatly, and may sometimes even appear to be wholly different from one another: but at other times there will be common elements. The elements themselves, which are the features of the building, stand for the experiences which we have, whether they are sought or not; and if we recall our description of them as being encounters with reality, we see that the separate diagrams of the building are in effect the different disciplines of study. Each discipline whether of art, poetry, history, science or philosophy, must try to achieve the fulness that is possible with its particular opportunities. No one picture is sufficient to describe the building completely, though a good "feel" for it may be obtained from a complete account according to one particular discipline. If we can agree to this, then we can see how it comes about that science, art, history and so on are to be called authentic revelations of God. We can also see that not all revelations will be the same, and in a very real sense each of us is bound to have his own. We shall expect to find certain common elements in our descriptions, and lots of others which are not common. Certain features of the building are best appreciated by one particular section, or elevation— which means that certain aspects of the nature of God will be best described within the framework, or pattern, of one particular study.

In all this we have spoken of art, poetry, history, science and philosophy as modes of description of the one reality. But we have said nothing about religion as such. This is quite intentional, for we shall have to wait a little before we can see the sense in which the word " religion " can be used within the terms of this analogy of the building.

But we can immediately see certain false statements made about religion. It is a false statement whenever it is claimed, or assumed without comment, that there is only one diagram to describe a building. For example, in a book concerned with religious illusions,[3] a distinguished scientist says : " only one description of the universe, or of any part of it, can be true." And Aldous Huxley[4] in one of his earlier books, asserts that " to talk about religion except in terms of human psychology, is an irrelevance." Professor C. D. Darlington, the well-known biologist,[5] claims that " the gradation between the most helpless of mortals and a Caesar (or a Newton or a Shakespeare) is a genetic one," and really nothing more. One could go on almost indefinitely like this, but one more example must suffice. Homer Smith, Professor of Physiology at the New York University College of Medicine, in his remarkable *Man and His Gods*,[6] can write, " In the long run of evolution *Homo sapiens* is simply a survival from the Neolithic age . . . civilisation is nothing more than the accumulation of experience and knowledge, it reflects nothing other than the use to which man has put his brain."

In effect all these writers are claiming that only one pattern can be used to link up every human experience. The correct answer to such people is to tell them that no one can force them to see the whole building if they don't want to do so; but that a very large number of their fellow scientists have indeed seen things that they themselves have not seen, and this is because they have come to their study prepared to make an open and not a partly closed response. This is not a question of learning, or ability, but of attitude. When, for example, at the end of his book *The Future of an Illusion*, Freud says : " No, science is no illusion : but it would be an illusion to suppose that we could get anywhere else what science cannot give us," we can soon spot the intruding false attitude, and be prepared to accept his account of religion as one, but not necessarily the only, nor even the most satisfying, account that could legitimately be given.

It may be worth giving a simple example to show the complementary character of the various accounts that can be given of one situation. I choose a primrose, because this will enable me to bring out the widely differing characteristics of what are, in a sense, parallel interpretations. To the question, " what is a primrose?" several valid answers may be given. One person says :

> A primrose by the river's brim
> A yellow primrose was to him,
> And it was nothing more.

Just that, and no more. Another person, the scientist, says " a primrose is a delicately balanced biochemical mechanism, requiring potash, phosphates, nitrogen and water in definite proportions." A third person says "a primrose is God's promise of spring." All three descriptions are correct, but they have about as much in common as three quite separate sections of the underground physics laboratory.

When they have thought about their work, many of the best scientists have recognised this alternative character of the descriptions which they give. Among the physicists it has become an almost universally accepted item of belief. For example we can point to the great controversy about light—was it corpuscular, as Newton believed; or wave-like, as Huygens claimed? Certainly some phenomena were better understood in one language, other phenomena in the alternative. But now a dualism is accepted : we use either the one or the other, choosing that which is best adapted to our particular situation. This does not mean that light is *both* corpuscle and wave : the dualism lies not in what Kant would call " the-thing-in-itself," but in our interpretation of it, in the language and concepts that we use to give meaning and pattern to experiments in optics and spectroscopy. It is just the same with the celebrated discussion about the nature of an electron; is that also a particle or is it a wave? The answer is precisely the same as before. " We don't know." For the thing-in-itself is as much unknown to us as is the physics laboratory at King's College, London, which, being entirely underground, cannot be " seen " in the usual sense of that word. What physicists have done is to devise models whereby the behaviour of the electron may be fitted to a pattern : and they have found that two different sets of concepts are needed to do justice to this behaviour. There was a time when this duality of description would have been rejected as wholly improper : and even now an occasional voice, such as that of Einstein, is raised against one or other aspect of the duality. But most of us have lived so long with this that we have grown used to it; and have come to see the great and liberating influence inherent in the two modes of description. The physicist, at least, would join battle, on my side, against those other scientists whom I quoted a moment ago, for whom the concept of " complementarity," which I have been describing, is still unrecognised.

Perhaps it is natural that the physicist should have been the first to remind us that, even within science—even within one branch of science—this concept of "sections of a building " must be introduced. For physics was the earliest science to develop any thorough-going discipline. But other scientists are coming to see it now, in greater numbers than before. Here, for example, is Tinbergen writing an account of what we mean by Instinct.[7] He begins by distinguishing three ways of studying behaviour that may be called instinctive. First we may seek the " causal structure " underlying it; what we might loosely refer to as the physics and chemistry of instinct. Then we may concentrate on the directiveness or biological purposiveness associated with it. This, which has a teleological character, is most important in any complete study of behaviour, but it is not a substitute for causal study. Finally there is the psychological way, quite distinct from the other two. Then he goes on :

The study of directiveness, the study of subjective
phenomena, and the study of causation are three
ways of thinking about behaviour, each of which
is consistent in the application of its own methods.
However, when they trespass into each other's
fields, confusion results.

Here too I would like to quote some excellent words
from the McNair lectures of my distinguished predecessor Professor E. W. Sinnott[3] of Yale :

Life can be studied fruitfully in its highest as well
as its lowest manifestations. The biochemist can
tell us much about protoplasmic organisation, but
so can the artist. Life is the business of the poet
as well as of the physiologist.

I believe that when Niels Bohr introduced this idea
of complementarity into physics, and then extended
it to apply more widely, he was opening a new
chapter in our understanding of the universe we live
in. Many of the celebrated debates of former days,
and the struggles of to-day, are essentially examples
of this duality. Both sides are right, but they have no
real contact with each other; and their points of view
are like two distinct sections of our physics laboratory,
with so little which is common that the protagonists
seem to a disinterested outsider to resemble a pair of
express trains travelling in opposite directions at high
speed past one another, but without having any real

" contact " at all. The whole matter is so important that I would like to illustrate it by reference to three such celebrated debates—mind and matter, free-will and determinism, and teleology.

First let us consider mind and matter. The issue is perfectly simple : mind is associated with body and brain, for we have no direct physical experience of a disembodied mind. But the brain is a most intricate collection of some 10^{10} of tiny electrical circuits, composed of nerves and so ultimately of atoms and molecules. The nature of a thought can be said to correspond to the patterns of electrical currents in these many circuits : for example, the activity of millions of neurons is involved in the recall of any memory; and sanity and insanity can be distinguished by the electro-encephalograph and revealed in the different kinds of rhythm which they exhibit. Sir Charles Sherrington in his Gifford Lectures has very vividly described the action of this vast assembly of resonating electrical circuits.[9] He speaks of it as an " enchanted loom where millions of flashing shuttles (i.e. nerve impulses) weave a dissolving pattern, always a meaningful pattern, though never an abiding one; a shifting harmony of sub-patterns." As for the details of behaviour of these many shuttles, we can use Leibniz' famous phrase, that " everything which takes place within my mind is as mechanical as what goes on inside a watch," though perhaps the word " mechanical " should be extended to include " electrical." Within this description what place can possibly be found for mind, as we are accustomed to regard it? The answer is that mind is a concept which we introduce, like other concepts such as gravitation, to make sense of our experiences. But these experiences are of many kinds, and if we use one single word "mind" to relate them together, we must not be surprised at confusion resulting. There are physico-chemical questions about mind, which will have physico-chemical answers : and artistic questions to receive artistic answers : and spiritual questions, with appropriate answers also. All the different sets of answers are like different sections of our building : all may be true, none is exhaustive. We must use them in their proper context, and not waste valuable time and effort[10] in the quite useless mixing of categories : to try to do this latter, and seek for a clear description of the traffic which passes along the brain-mind highway, is to court confusion, as when Eddington[11] is led to speak of a "correlated behaviour of the individual particles of matter" in a manner which must be regarded by us as "something outside physics," or as when Professor Eccles[12] tries to avoid the Cartesian dualism of mind and matter by introducing a "detector that has a sensitivity of a different kind from that of any physical instrument." How much better it is to have done with this dichotomy, and to turn to the liberating influence of Prince de Broglie,[13] telling us : "I do not see how consciousness can be derived from material things. I regard consciousness and matter as different aspects of the same thing"; or of Gilbert Ryle[14] asserting that "mind is not matter interpreted by the quantum theory," or any other theory. Mind and matter are different ways of looking at the same set of phenomena, or experiences (i.e. man). Mind is not a sort of "ghost in the machine" called matter. Man is matter, or mind, according to the situation you are describing, and the pattern within which you give it meaning. I am sure that in a few years' time we shall be grateful for this widening of our discourse.

Much the same can be said about my second "famous debate," that between free-will and determinism.[15] As Max Planck pointed out several years ago,[16] this is as much a phantom problem as that between mind and matter. Let us think of Julius Caesar about to cross the Rubicon. The historian giving us this part of Roman history, and making use of the best scientific research into the situation of the time, will speak of political issues and innate temperament which effectively compelled Caesar's decision to burn his boats. Indeed, our historian is accounted a good historian just in so far as he can make the decision appear inevitable. But, with no less validity, we may try to project ourselves into Caesar's mind. One thing and one thing only, stands out in sharp relief : he has to decide. Political eventualities are the material of his decision, to be borne in mind and weighed up : but they do not themselves force him either way : at most they urge this or that action. It is a plain disregard of evidence and experience to deprive him of his moment of anxiety and decision. So what can we say of all this? Observed from without, the will is causally determined; observed from within it is free. The difference lies in the point of view (the section of the building) for no answer at all can be given until we have specified explicitly the viewpoint of our observation, and said whether we are actor or spectator. For man as actor the best con-

cept is freewill : but for man as spectator it is deter-
minacy. Once again let us be glad for the new
development. As always the truth has made us free,
but within a wider framework than could have been
possible before. At very least it lets us see the fallacy
in Voltaire's famous aphorism : " it would be very
singular that all nature, all the planets should obey
eternal laws, and that there should be a little animal,
five feet high, who, in contempt of these laws, could
act as he pleased, solely according to his caprice."

The last of my three phantom problems is that of
teleology—whether, in Charles Kingsley's words we
are obliged to choose between " the absolute empire
of accident and a living, immanent, ever-working
God."[17] With all respects to the author of *Madame
How and Lady Why* I believe that this choice is one
that we may make at our absolute discretion : for
the two accounts of the development of the natural
order are not to be regarded as exclusive. For some
purposes one of these is better than the other, but in
other circumstances the reverse will hold. This is an
important point and worth elaborating a little. First
let us see the nature of the choice in a purely physico-
mathematical situation; and then return to biology.

Consider the path traced out by a ray of light
which passes from a penny at the bottom of a pond
to the eye of the man who is standing at the edge of
the pond looking for it. There are two ways in
which we may describe this path. On the one hand
we may say that the transmission of light is given by
a certain partial differential equation. This equation
is a purely " local " one, in that it can be written

down independently of where the penny or the observer's eye may be. There is no teleological element within this description. For the light from the penny spreads out in a beam uniformly all round the penny, is bent on hitting the surface of the water and then continues in an ever-spreading beam in the air. But there is an alternative mode which we could use. This is based on Fermat's principle, which states, in non-technical language, that the ray of light from the penny to the eye will follow that particular path which makes a certain function as small as possible, i.e. a minimum. But this means that our description of the path is one which we can only begin to draw, once it has left the penny, if we already know the position of the eye which is to receive it. Now it has become almost fair to say that the path is determined by the end which is to be reached, though of course it is not a straight path on account of the bending which takes place as it passes from the water into the air. In this description there is a very distinct teleological element. But the important point is this; we may choose either mode and be entirely fair to the observation of the penny by the eye. What we are accustomed to call geometrical and physical optics are complementary descriptions; either may be used, but only one at a time!

Having dealt with this relatively non-emotive situation we are ready to turn to the more interesting biological situation, where, if we are not careful, we can soon let feelings run high. But I believe that precisely the same conditions apply. I think, for example, that if we wanted, we could describe evolution in those terms which I quoted earlier in this chapter: "*Homo sapiens* is simply a survival from the Neolithic Age"; but in doing so we must be careful not to use the adverb "simply" to imply that no other description is valid. In actual fact, I don't believe that this particular description is very helpful, nor that it does justice to the pattern even of technical biology. I am more impressed by the words of Sherrington[18] when he is discussing the evolution of cells in a human body and writes: "It is as if an immanent principle inspired each cell with knowledge for the carrying out of a design"; and, again:

We seem to watch battalions of specific catalysts, like Maxwell's demons, lined up, each waiting, stop-watch in hand, for its moment to play the part assigned to it, a step in one or other great thousand-linked chain process. . . . In the spongework of the cell, foci coexist for different operations, so that a hundred, or a thousand different processes go forward at the same time within its confines. The foci wax and wane as they are wanted . . . the processes going forward in it are co-operatively harmonised. The total system is organised. The various catalysts work as co-ordinatedly as though each had its own compartment in the honeycomb and its own turn and time. In this great company, along with stop-watches run dials telling how confreres and their substrates are getting on, so that at zero time each takes its turn. Let that catastrophe befall which is death, and these catalysts become a disorderly mob and pull the very fabric of the cell to pieces. Whereas in life as well as pulling down they build and build to a plan.

Anyone who has thought for ten minutes about the structure of the eye, or the building of a cobweb, or the unique parasitism of the Common Cuckoo, in which as Raven has shown,[19] a sequence of at least five distinct events is essential to the success of the whole performance, and not one of them lies inside the run of normal behaviour and structure, will be tempted into teleological language. Even Professor Bernal speaks of "a principle of order latent in the very atoms of which a protein is made"; Joseph Needham[20] talks of "the striving of a blastula to grow into a chicken"; and Carus[21] tells us to take "the purest, most indifferent fluid, water: over it there hovers, or had we better say, in it there lives, the picture of actual crystallisation according to the law of triangular and hexagonal symmetry; and as the floating drop of water is subjected to the effect of cold . . . there appears the delicate form of the water crystal as snowflakes, as three- or six-pointed star. The picture, the type, or idea of this form was therefore present, before the form appeared." Yet the water molecule, which behaves in this fashion, is well understood by physicists and chemists, and the law of force between it and its neighbouring molecules can be studied. Whether we use the language of teleology or not is a matter for our choice. But unless we do, we shall miss part of the pattern of nature shown by science. My claim that different approaches require different patterns of description (different sections of the building) receives some support from the fact that the same person uses two or more apparently irreconcilable descriptions, at different times, for the same phenomena. Everyone is familiar with Huxley's Romanes lecture of 1893, *Evolution and Ethics,* with its insistence on "nature, red in tooth and claw," and on the interpretation of evolution as a struggle for survival with no holds barred. But not everyone realises that Huxley could also write like this[22] about the conditions for evolution as we have seen it : " In place of ruthless self-assertion it demands self-restraint; in place of thrusting aside or treading down or competition, it requires that the individual shall not merely respect but shall help his fellows; its influence is directed not so much to the survival of the fittest, as to the fitting of as many as possible to survive." In view of these conflicting descriptions either we must judge their author to be undecided and vacillating in his conclusions, or we may feel that both accounts are true, but valid within different frameworks. I prefer the latter alternative.

We have now reached the condition of recognising the validity of different conceptual patterns associated with substantially the same phenomena. But it is quite obvious that not all patterns are equally suitable. Indeed it would not be a bad definition of " wisdom " to say that it consists in knowing which concepts to use for any required purpose. Concepts out of context are as disastrous as mixing drinks. " A sensible philosophy," says Dr. N. W. Pirie,[23] " controlled by a relevant set of concepts saves so much research time that it can nearly act as a substitute for genius . . . we avoid the problems which are real in adjacent fields but are pseudo in our own." If this is true even in science itself, how much more true must it be when we are concerned with as wide a field as science and religion. And it is particularly true when we are discussing human motives and human thoughts.

An example will show what I mean. When you listen to me speaking you could perfectly correctly say: "I was listening to a man blowing air through a hole in his head." For indeed that is precisely what happens when I speak; I do turn myself into a bellows and make noises which travel at a measurable speed. But for almost all purposes, it is wiser—as we put it, more sensible—to say: "I was listening to someone speaking."

We all know this in the conduct of our own lives, for the mental framework in which a young man goes to watch a football match is different from that in which he meets his girl friend. Yet it is the same person in both cases. The one description does not invalidate the other. When I am in the Mathematical Institute at Oxford my mental framework is quite different from that when I am digging my garden; there is a vast difference between discussing the motion of a particle in wave mechanics and reading William Blake:

> I see a World in a grain of sand,
> And a Heaven in a wild flower.

But it is always the same person who is involved. To fail to change my mental framework is to ossify, and not to live. Alas that it is so easy to lose this liberat-

ing power, as a recent discussion between a group of
scientists and a group of poets shows.[24] (In fact, this
is about all that this particular discussion does
show!) I should like to refer to one of the most
clearcut illustrations of the results of this refusal to
consider more than one conceptual scheme. It is in
what we may call the denial of God. It seems to me
entirely possible—and I shall give reasons later for
believing that this is the case—that within any one
scheme or discipline, we may not see God at once:
or, if we see Him, may fail to recognise Him. In
most cases, if not all, there is no compelling reason
why we should. The astronomer who turns from his
telescope and exclaims: "I swept the heavens and
found no God"; and the man who, after focusing
his microscope, rises with the exclamation, "I have
examined the brain and found no traces of love"[25]
are both right, although both God and love can exist
within the pictures that they see. We need to remember that Laplace, asserting that he "had no need
of that hypothesis" (God), and Descartes, crying
"Give me matter and motion, and I'll construct the
universe," were both professing Christians; and,
within certain limits, they spoke correctly. It is on
this issue that the Christian will take exception to the
Scientific Humanists. This does not mean that he
denies their science: but it does mean that he de-
plores their narrow-mindedness. What, for example,
could be more futile and impoverished than this sort
of cry from one of our English poet-scientists? "Scientific Humanists do not reject Christianity because of its
moral claims on the individual, but because we cannot

accept a God whose working in the Universe is not merely inscrutable, but so well concealed as to leave no vestige of observable material to the unconvinced observer?" He might as well have asked us to weigh the soul. If we had been successful it would have been a disaster of the first magnitude, for it would have shown that the soul belonged to the concepts and framework of physics : and part at least of the richness and colour of life would have been lost. I prefer the less pretentious claims of Werner Heisenberg :[26]

> The concepts "soul" or "life" do not occur in atomic physics, and they could not, even indirectly, be derived as complicated consequences of some natural law. Their existence certainly does not indicate the presence of any fundamental substance other than energy, but it shows only the action of other kinds of forms which we cannot match with the mathematical forms of modern atomic physics. . . . If we want to describe living or mental processes, we shall have to broaden these structures. It may be that we shall have to introduce yet other concepts.

What a magnificent opening for Christian apologetics! And how tragic that, for fear, so few of us have tried to make our case. Perhaps the fault lies in ourselves, for our too limited vision of God. The man who wrote the book *Your God is too Small* was speaking to the condition of most of us. A denial of God is practically always the result of shutting one eye. It may be for this reason that God gave us two.

At this stage we must leave the line of development which we have been following in order to deal with an apparent inconsistency. To resolve the paradox we shall have to return to our earlier promise, and say something about the way in which "religion" fits into the analogy of the building with its various plans and elevations. This analogy has underlain almost everything so far in this chapter. The apparent inconsistency arises from our claim that science is an essentially religious activity (see chapter 2), and yet that neither the astronomer with his telescope nor the physiologist with his microscope are necessarily led to recognise God in their work. The resolution of the paradox lies in the recognition that although science may be a religious activity, it is not religion. Here we are on very delicate ground, for it is remarkably difficult to say just what we really mean by religion. Most of the familiar clichés are unsatisfactory : Religion is " the acceptance of God," "the link that binds a man to his God," "faith in God," "what a man does with his solitariness," "eternal life"—none of these seem to me to be satisfying because not one of them does justice to the grandeur both of earth and heaven. At the risk of adding yet further to our confusion, I will suggest another definition : "Religion is the total response of man to all his environment." At first sight that may seem very tame.[27] And certainly before we can say much about any particular form of religion, such as Christianity, we shall have to add to this definition. But by saying that it is the "total" response we imply the response of his whole being, his body, his mind, his concepts, his emotions, his imagination, his human relationships, everything indeed that can be said about him in terms of the wholeness of his being, which is distinct from his environment. And by saying "all his environment" we imply all that a man may know or experience as being other than himself; as St. Paul would put it, "both things on earth, and things in heaven."

But this sounds all too formal. Fortunately, however, if we may return to the analogy of the building, we can understand it better. Each section of that physics laboratory in London is necessarily a two-dimensional affair. It is an abstraction of certain elements from the totality. If we call it a representation of the laboratory, then it is obviously partial. And however perfect we make our one single drawing it can never give us a satisfactory description of the building. Indeed, the greater technicalities of the diagram may sometimes serve to impede our sense of the total edifice, in much the same way that wearing blinkers helps the horse to see clearly what is directly in front at the expense of narrowing his field of view. But the building does become three-dimensional when we can place ourselves in the attitude to accept more than one "view." This, of course, is exactly what we do with our eyes in stereoscopic vision. We gain the sense of perspective and solidity and distance just because our two eyes see things slightly differently, and we accept the two accounts. We do not superimpose them—for that would make nonsense of what we see—but in some sense we do hold them together. I believe that something akin to this is necessary if we would find God. In some stereoscopic way we must build up out of the imperfect abstractions of any one conceptual framework, something of the full three-dimensional character of the reality which we continually encounter in every experience. I want some word to represent this synoptic function. For lack of any better alternative, let us call it the "act of reflection," though since it is a "total response" of which we are talking, "reflection" must include both normal mental activity of the discursive type and other, non-discursive, modes of knowing also. Thus the act of reflection is the putting together of two or more partial views : it is the connecting of religious activities with religion : in Bacon's words, it is the being "led from a study of the created works to a contemplation of the Creator" : or in the words of the Scottish mathematician Colin Maclaurin in the early eighteenth century, "it is a piece of real worship to contemplate the great beautiful drama of nature."[28] The act of reflection, as I have described it here, is akin to the gaining of "insight," a very different matter from the gaining of knowledge. This is why we call it a total response to all our environment.

There are many ways of expressing this, but in one form or another all of them refer back to the experiences involved in understanding our environment. For as Kant would put it, the experiences are primary, they are all we have : and in our own earlier phrase, the experiences transcribe for us our multitudinous encounters with reality. Here are three quite different examples of the way in which the fundamental "act of reflection" is described.

Scattered among Egyptian dust heaps, and on odd bricks and papyri, there are sometimes found so-called words of Jesus. Some are genuine, many are doubtful, but nearly always they give an insight that is true to the spirit of many of His more historical sayings. Consider this, for example : " Who are they which draw you to the Kingdom? The Kingdom is in heaven; but they that are on earth, and the birds of the heaven and the fishes of the sea, these are they that draw you to it." Here it is the use of the word " draw," with its sense of some deeper interpretation, which is significant.

It is a long way from Egypt to Martin Luther, but the following words come from his Preface to the *Magnificat* : " No one can understand God or God's word unless he has it revealed to him by the Holy Ghost. (This suggests that our ' total response ' is the work of the Holy Ghost, who, we are told, will ' lead us into all truth.') But nobody can receive anything from the Holy Ghost unless he experiences it."

My last example of this act of reflection is very typical of the scientist. It concerns Jean Henri Fabre, the entomologist. After he had studied the process of cross-pollination of flowers by insects, there came over him a sense of almost incredulous awe. " Before these mysteries of life," he cried, " reason bows and abandons itself to adoration of the Author of these miracles."

It is important to realise that in each of these examples of the act of reflection, we have started with our experiences of our environment; and that in none of them have we rejected the picture given by science. It is precisely because this picture exists, and can be received, and placed beside other pictures that God, so to speak, steps down from the two-dimensional screen into solid three-dimensional life.

When a scientist asserts that he is not religious, we shall want to say of him that he has not, or cannot, make the full act of reflection. His response to his environment may be generous, but it is not total. This raises the questions, how can we make it total? and what conditions are involved? Clearly an open-mindedness is essential, some sort of willingness to be led to that strange world where separate pictures merge without losing their validity. But there is more to it than that. We need some attitude of mind which does not always come easily to the specialist, whether he be scientist, artist or historian. The greater the necessary degree of specialisation, the more formal the language in which a man describes his work, the more difficult will it be for him to prepare himself for this new adventure in understanding. Of course the scientist should not be surprised about the need for a proper attitude. For he knows it even in his own speciality. Did not Pasteur say: "Chance only visits the prepared mind"? and Claude Nicolle: "Chance favours only those who know how to court her"? When we have prepared our minds to receive our inspiration, then, in Helmholtz's well-known words: "Happy ideas come unexpectedly without effort, like an inspiration"; or as in a phrase of Sir Malcolm Sadler:[29] "the ideas come to me unsought and I find them in my mind exactly as I might find a half-crown that someone had put into my pocket while my coat was hanging up in my absence." But perhaps the loveliest of all such accounts of the attitude of mind and the patience which is involved before it issues in success, is to be found in some of the letters of William Herschel writing about the results of stellar observations with his own home-made telescopes : [30]

Seeing is in some respects an art which must be learnt. To make a person see with such a power [as his] is nearly the same as if I were asked to make him play one of Handel's fugues upon the organ. Many a night have I been practising to see . . .

These instruments have played me so many tricks that I have at last found them out in many of their humours and have made them confess to me what they would have concealed if I had not with such perseverance and patience courted them. I have tortured them with powers, flattered them with attendance to find out the critical moments when they would act . . . it would be hard if they had not been kind to me at least.

When we carry all this out of the particular problem of astronomy into the more general one of the "act of reflection," we find that we are really talking about faith and hope. For faith, as John Wesley said long ago, is an active principle, and hope relates to that which we do not yet possess. Once more science and religion are found speaking the same language.

I have spoken of the act of reflection in which we find God as if it were almost optional : and of the attitude of mind which is pre-requisite as if it were something that some people might feel desirable and worthwhile, but which others would not care to make the effort to obtain. This is to do injustice to our status as human beings. Unless the act of reflection takes place, we cannot deal adequately with the variety and magnitude of human existence, nor can we discover what may properly be called " meaning in life " : certainly we cannot do justice to our full experience as human beings. F. A. Cockin, Bishop of Bristol, tells how one day he was sitting in a London tram when a very immaculate gentleman entered, resplendent in his pin-stripe trousers, bowler hat and tightly rolled umbrella. A small boy, sitting opposite, eyed him most suspiciously for a minute or two and then, in that high-pitched querulous tone of voice which small boys reserve for really important occasions, he turned to his mother and said : " Mummy, what's that man for?" He was right. There are questions about man which do not come into the normal categories of science—perfectly valid questions, which do not allow those people who have once perceived them to rest until some satisfying answer has been given. We might almost say that something extra was needed, not to change our previous answers, or patterns, but to supplement them, to interpret them and to enhance their significance. In Samuel Butler's words : " The highest thought is ineffable. It must be felt from one person to another, but cannot be articulated—our profoundest and most important convictions are unspeakable."

Examples crowd themselves upon us. In music, for instance, why does the octave sound pleasant to us?

If we say that it is because the two frequencies are in the exact ratio two to one, we do not give a satisfactory answer, though it may be a correct one. When two lovers meet, shall we merely describe the event in terms of an accelerated release of adrenalin into the blood? It is true, but how pitifully inadequate! When we see a mother caring for her child, shall we speak only of the preservation of the race? When we think of the powerful mind of an Einstein or a Shakespeare, is it nothing more than an intricate network of nerve endings and innumerable pulsating electrical circuits that we envisage? It is all this, without a doubt. But all these things—and others too, keep on telling us that what we have been saying about them is true, but it is not enough : that man lives in two worlds (or perhaps more); and that there is a field, or world, of science in which questions posed in scientific terms get scientific answers; and another world, where words like belief, love, splendour and majesty have meaning. This other world refuses to be shut out of our experience; and if men try to do so, then even what they have discovered will be taken from them.

Yet these worlds impinge : they are not disparate. And the act of reflection brings them together. When, at the end of his *Origin of Species,* Darwin speaks of the "grandeur" of the economy of life that he has been describing : when one of the section leaders of the British Association three years ago chooses for the title of his Presidential address : *Organic Design,* we ought to see a reaching out to something beyond. Even when Huxley and Darwin try to interpret whole realms of biological activity under the title "struggle for existence," we should be willing to recognise kinship with at least one of the main themes of religious thought. When J. Z. Young[31] speaks of man as made for co-operation and communication with his fellows, he is glimpsing something of the Christian experience of fellowship and the Christian doctrine of Heaven. When Jeans writes of the "Mysterious Universe," and when Fred Hoyle[32] speaks of its "fineness," both "in concept and design," they are not far from the Kingdom.

To refuse to make this co-ordinating act and to stick to one view, one discipline, one "section of the building," is bound to lead to dissatisfaction, and this will be most deeply felt in our understanding of man. It is precisely because we are human that this situation arises: and because, being human, we are involved in everything else. Terence was right—*Homo sum : humani nil a me alienum puto.* If we think for a moment of our friends, then, as Eddington warned us, the scientific method may be applied to them : they may be described in psychological terms and they may be systematised and scheduled in biochemical language, so that, in one sense, we know all about them. But in another, and deeper sense, we shall then know nothing. Our examination will have thrown light on the nature of scientific thinking, it is most unlikely that it will have said very much about our friends.

Nowhere is the need for my "act of reflection" so essential as when we ask what we can say about life, and particularly human life. We must deal with this matter now because it brings up an exceedingly important issue for the concluding chapter of this book.

In everything that has been said so far we have
treated the scientist as if he was an explorer. His task
was to accept experiences, related to some reality outside him, and then to find meaning for them in some
acceptable pattern. This is a progressive task, and
we may hope that as time goes on, he will be able to
give an increasingly full and detailed account of the
physical basis of life. As Heisenberg has said: "the
chain of being which connects the atom with man is
continuous."[33] And Bernal[34] has shown how far we
can go, even now, in providing an account of life in
physical and chemical terms. But there is more to our
discussion than that. For the scientist is himself part
of the process which he is describing. When we give
an account of life we are trying to give an account
of something which includes ourselves. In this strange
region the dualism which we can usually almost succeed in establishing between observer and observed
is abolished. It is replaced by a most interesting
mutual relationship in which observer and observed
mingle. For man discusses nature and makes laws
to describe it; but on the other hand he is himself
part of this nature and has actually evolved out of it.

This bald statement of the position must be developed. There are two sides to the relationship that we
are considering. As Weiszäcker puts it[35] they are like
two semi-circular arcs, both of which are needed if
we would make from them a complete circle. In the
first half-circle we think of nature as something discussed by man. There is no need to say much about
this now because it was central to our argument in
Chapter 2. It is human hands that adjust every
piece of apparatus in an experiment, human eyes

that read the scale, or the clock, or the gauge, it is a human mind that first thought of doing the experiment, and it is a human mind which finally invents the law which describes its results in the simplest form that it can devise. *We* make the laws. We could almost say that Nature was a product of man's mind—and certainly our laws of Nature enable us to control and alter nature in an increasing degree.

But in the second half-circle we realise that man has gradually evolved out of nature. Time was when he did not exist. The great age of the universe and the gradual emergence of life from very humble beginnings right up to man with the power of thought and imagination; all this is a tremendous picture of evolution. We are part and parcel of the Universe that we are busy describing; and the description that we give of ourselves, if it is a scientific description, will be one in which our emergence as human beings is the result of certain scientific laws. We may describe these laws, but we who make the description are the product of these same laws.

It is a bit like arguing in a circle. On the one hand " natural science is itself made by man and for man, and is subject to the conditions of every intellectual and material work of man. Man is older than natural science." On the other hand " man is himself a being of nature. Nature is older than man. Man is come out of nature and is subject to her laws. An entire science, medical science, is successfully engaged in studying man as part of nature, with the methods of natural science." As Eddington puts it :[36] " We have found a strange footprint on the shores of the unknown. We have devised profound theories, one after another, to account for its origin. At last we have succeeded in reconstructing the creature that made the footprint. And lo! It is our own."

It comes to this, that nature had to be so that there could be man—man had to be so that there could be concepts of nature. Our plight is worse than that of the hapless biology student who saw long curved black lines in every object which he examined under the microscope but had no way of telling that it was his own eyelashes always getting in the way.

The significant point about all this is that man is never merely an observer of what goes on: he can never relinquish his part in the play, for he is an actor as well as a thinker. Descartes could use the argument, *cogito, ergo sum,* as the basis of his philosophy. But it seems to me now that he only said one half of what there is to say. This other part, which is just as important if we would understand the true status of man, is man's response to his existence. Ortega y Gasset[37] puts this very plainly:

The most trivial, and at the same time the most important note in human life is that man has no choice but to be always doing something to keep himself in existence . . . life is given us . . . but it is not given us ready made . . . we find ourselves under compulsion to do something, but never under compulsion to do something in particular.

So Descartes describes man-the-spectator, man-the-observer, with the power to use his thinking to make a descriptive pattern of the universe in which he lives.

But man is more : he is all the time responding to his environment : he foresees, he decides, he acts, he controls. We are not truly human unless we are both actor and spectator. This is clear enough if we recall the terms in which we describe a man who always seems to be separate from the things that go on in the world; watching them carefully, sometimes studying them, but quite unperturbed and unaffected by them, unsympathetic, apparently neither rejoicing nor being sad about events. We say : what an inhuman sort of man he is ! Here again is our dual rôle. We cannot describe ourselves unless we take account both of our ability to think and make scientific laws, and also of our ability to make decisions and react towards people and circumstances. Dr. F. H. Heinemann has put this very neatly by varying Descartes' argument to read : *Respondeo, ergo sum.*

We can reach just the same sort of conclusion in a quite different way. Suppose that we are studying a piece of crystal, or a flower. By studying them, and formulating laws about them, we cannot be said to alter them. They are effectively the same after we have finished studying them as they were before we began. But suppose instead that we try to study ourselves, and ask ourselves questions about ourselves. Then immediately we begin to affect and change ourselves. If we merely do such an innocent thing as ask ourselves if we like the flower, or think the shape of the little crystal attractive, then we force ourselves to make up our mind. We are no longer spectators asking questions about something in which we are not personally involved—we are actors, making decisions, being influenced by our environment, becoming different people from what we were before we started asking these questions. It is almost as if we could never quite catch up with ourselves. Because of man's dual rôle no scientific account of man will ever be able to describe him as he is—the best that it can hope for is to describe him as he was.

There is another way of looking at this situation. Suppose that I am trying to make a scientific study of myself. I shall, of course, have to ask myself questions, making experiments on myself to test my reactions to this or that stimulus. When I have made the experiments and asked the questions, some part of me must receive the answers and draw correct conclusions from them. If it is the " I " who is asking the questions, there must always be a bit of myself—the bit that does the asking—which I cannot examine. A large part of myself may be the " examinee," but there must always be a bit left over to be the " examiner." Science can be used to describe the first of these, but it cannot describe the second. Or, more precisely, it can only describe it in the past, never in the present. As Herbert Dingle[38] has said, there is a " non objectivisable ' I ' of whom I have immediate knowledge, different in character from my knowledge of anything else. To say that it is non-objectivisable is to say that I cannot talk about it, for immediately I do so it becomes the object of my speech and is no longer ' I ' but ' me. ' "

So we see the extreme importance of his dual rôle in any proper understanding of man. Earlier in this chapter I gave three parallel answers to the question, what is a primrose? We are now ready to see the

answers to the profounder question, what is man?
The physicist will describe him as a machine for
doing work, the chemist as a means of converting
chemical energy into other forms of energy, the biologist will speak of him as the latest—and perhaps
the last—product of the evolutionary process. All
three pictures—and of course there are more than
these three—arise from one or other of the grand
conceptual schemes of science, and they reflect the
religious character of all true study as we have described it before. But the Christian, making his act
of reflection and his total response to this almost be-
wilderingly rich variety of pattern, will want to say:
he is a child of God.

But we must be careful. The physicist, as such,
gives only one of these answers, the chemist and biologist only one. The Christian gives them all. He can
agree unreservedly with these others, and rejoice that
their accounts are so splendid. He will say that he
needs all these partial descriptions, these " two-dimensional " abstractions from the " three-dimensional "
character of man's full stature, before he can claim
to understand him properly. And as for those more
puzzling questions about the control, and the use or
the misuse, of man, these cannot be answered and a
true response made, unless the partial descriptions
are available. The religious view of man is not separate from, or contrary to, the scientific. It is the act
of reflection and total response, not only to the scientific view, but to all other forms of revelation accessible to the " I " as well as to the " Me." In the
development of this response and the knowledge on
which it is partly based, the scientist has his own

particular rôle—and it is an important one. Did not G. K. Chesterton[39] speak about him in these terms:

> Far away in some strange constellation in skies infinitely remote, there is a small star, which astronomers may some day discover. At least, I could never observe in the faces or demeanour of most astronomers or men of science any evidence that they had discovered it; though as a matter of fact they were walking about on it all the time. It is a star that brings forth out of itself very strange plants and very strange animals; and none stranger than the men of science.

CHAPTER FOUR

Christian Belief

THE time has come for us to try and gather up the train of thought of earlier chapters, and see whether it allows us to make any statement of the Christian faith which would be acceptable to those trained in the discipline of science. Now there are some people who believe that such a project is unseemly. Kant has described their position, and also the grounds whereby it cannot be justified :

> Religion on the ground of its sanctity, and law on the ground of its majesty, often resist the sifting of their claims by critical thought. But in doing so they inevitably awake a not unjust suspicion that their claims are ill-founded, and they cease to command the unfeigned homage which is paid by Reason to that which has shown itself able to stand the test of free enquiry.

If we cannot provide an account of our faith in terms that may be understood by the professional scientist, then we abdicate our claim to give a comprehensive interpretation of the whole of human experience. This would be a tragedy.

In order to discover the true relationship of science and religion we began by discussing science as a way of knowing : we recognised it as one form of abstrac-

tion from the greater body of reality, and we likened
it to what is seen in one of the architect's drawings
of a building. There are other drawings, as well as
this one, which though they are equally correctly
described as representations of the building, yet may
seem quite different from the first. We do not get
the "feel" of the building by a geometrical super-
position of the drawings : nor do we see the relationship of science and the Christian faith by a simple
addition process. The late Lord Lindsay, formerly
Master of Balliol, used sometimes to refer to the Scottish minister who began his prayer "O Lord, who
art our ultimate hypothesis and our eternal hope . . ."
This mixing of disciplines does justice neither to the
imaginative and creative aspect of science, nor to the
sense of awe and exaltation which men experience
when they feel themselves in the presence of the living
God. The discovery of "religion" from within the
"religious study" which is called science, comes to
us in what I called the act of reflection. We must
therefore start our present discussion with a more
careful analysis of the characteristics of this act. We
shall then be able to see that it leads us stage by stage
through Natural Theology to Christian belief.

We must begin with Natural Theology—that which
Francis Bacon[1] defined as the "spark of knowledge
of God which may be had by the light of nature, and
the consideration of created things : and thus can be
fairly held to be divine in respect of its object, and
natural in respect of its source of information"—
because whatever we may find in our journey must
inevitably be bound up with the measurements, the

observations, the experiences which are the starting point of science.

But the first thing to notice about these experiences is a sense of "given-ness." Almost everyone, whether scientist, artist or poet, is aware of this. In Chapter 2 I quoted Beethoven's description of music as a " revelation "; but I could equally have quoted from Sir Lawrence Bragg,[2] Lord Rutherford's successor in the Cavendish Laboratory at Cambridge :

> When one has sought long for the clue to a secret of nature, and is rewarded by grasping some part of the answer, it comes as a blinding flash of revelation : it comes as something new, more simple and at the same time more aesthetically satisfying than anything one could have created in one's own mind. This conviction is of something revealed, and not something imagined.

So it seems as if the inner truths of our concepts and our brilliant imagination are really not our own at all : they are something which we could not find for ourselves, unless it were given to us in the search. This has been well brought out in a recent lecture on poetry by C. Day Lewis,[3] the Professor of Poetry at Oxford. " The poet is trying to make sense, poetic sense, out of his experiences . . . (he) is usually not just putting truth into verse, as a dressmaker might build a dress round a model; he is discovering truth through verse." It comes to this, that in every encounter with reality, in whatever discipline, we find that the reality comes to meet us; it is given.

The second thing to say about the act of reflection is that the separate patterns, or disciplines, on which it rests, express a unity. In the language of our analogy of the physics laboratory at London, there is only one building though there are many sectional diagrams and drawings. It is one of the deepest convictions of scientists that, ultimately, their science is one. This is true at all levels—within one science; as between one science and another; and in regard to the relation between man and nature. The first level, within one science, is illustrated by a remark of Michael Faraday, in 1816 at his first lecture to the City Philosophical Society, where we catch a glimpse of his intuitive belief in the essential unity of the physical forces of nature : " That the attraction of aggregation and chemical affinity is actually the same as the attraction of gravitation and electrical attraction, I will not positively affirm, but I believe they are." The second level, as between one science and another, can be seen in the speech made by Rev. W. Vernon Harcourt,[4] chemist and Canon of York, when proposing the establishment of the British Association in 1831 : " The chief interpreters of nature have always been those who grasped the widest field of enquiry, who felt an interest in every question which the one great system of Nature presents." And the third level, in regard to the relation between man and zoological nature, is illustrated by Sir Ronald Fisher in his recent Croonian Lecture :[5] " The moral I should draw from these examples, [i.e. what he has been discussing in this lecture] is a trite one in this company, though often overlooked elsewhere; that our best way towards understanding our own species is often through the study of what St. Francis might have called our little brother, the grouse locust, and even our little sister, the bacteriophage."

Running through all these quotations, and indeed, almost all the work of scientists, is a sense of the unity of life, and the gross inadequacy therefore, of any one view, or discipline, to express this unity by itself. The scientist who asserts: "The argument still stands up that intellect is *simply* a very complex expression of the regulating character of all protoplasmic activity" is not playing fair with this conviction of unity since he claims that intellect belongs wholly to the world of biochemistry.[6] It would be better to say, with Descartes towards the end of his life, after his original dualism had been somewhat modified: "I am lodged in my body, not as a pilot in a ship, but so intimately conjoined and as it were, intermingled with it that with it I form a unitary whole." The French critic and journalist[7] who said that "politics is not applied geometry, but the practice of medicine or a rule of hygiene" has seen something about life which comes to those who will "receive and reflect" in a manner different from those who only "receive" the revelations in science, art, history and the rest.

This leads us to the third stage in our enquiry. Not only do our separate disciplines reveal a unity; but that unity has a quality about it which can only be described as spiritual. We have already quoted from Mr. Bernard Barber to the effect that "science is a moral enterprise": but we could equally well have quoted from Einstein:[8]

You will hardly find one among the profounder sort of scientific minds, without peculiar religious feeling of his own. . . . His religious feeling takes the form of rapturous amazement at the harmony of the natural law. . . . This feeling is the guiding principle of his life and work. It is beyond question akin to that which has possessed the religious geniuses of all ages.

Not every scientist would put it so directly in these terms. But the emotion which they describe is general : and that is enough for our present argument. Of course the " act of reflection " is implicit in such a feeling. Without such an act, science (or any other philosophy) is merely a set of connections, or a series of logical forms, a sort of " ballet of bloodless categories," if we may use F. H. Bradley's vivid phrase. But with this act, it becomes the carrier of spiritual meaning : Nature itself requires a religious significance. We shall want to echo the words of Pasteur : " I see everywhere the inevitable expression of the Infinite in the world : through it the supernatural is at the bottom of every heart." But we shall certainly not want to repeat the words of a Christian writer[9] who discusses the scientific attitude and says : " It is wise to confine attention to the case where . . . the reality of God affects the matter at issue." For " it is important for men to learn how and when to act with sober scientific wisdom. It is equally important that they should learn how and when to act with sober Christian faith." I cannot believe that such is our real choice. This is a false antithesis. If my argument is sound, then the " reality of God " affects every issue, since whatever we see, wherever we look, whether we recognise it as true or not, we cannot touch or handle the things of earth and not, in that very moment, be confronted with the sacraments of heaven.

This, as Dean Inge[10] has said, is the failure of Rationalism, that it tries " to find a place for God in its picture of the world. But God, whose centre is everywhere and His circumference nowhere, cannot be fitted into a diagram. He is rather the canvas on which the picture is painted, or the frame in which it is set." To see this is to enter a new world of freedom and wonder, in every corner of which God may be found. We can no more agree with Pascal : " Corporeal things are only an image of spiritual . . . we must consider ourselves as criminals in a prison full of images of their liberator." Instead we begin to grasp what is implied in the apocryphal saying of Jesus : " Raise the stone and thou shalt find me : cleave the wood and I am there." We begin to see how the idea of an incarnation is the only way in which we can make sense of the grandeur that is all around us; and how, if there is such an incarnation, then " neither height nor depth," nor " principalities and powers " can ever separate us from its author.

It is true that this has not got us to the Christian faith. In one sense it has only got us as far as pantheism. But it has got us started, and it leads us to the next stage in our argument; that the spiritual quality of the unity we experience, and to which science contributes, must be expressed in terms that are at least personal. I have used the words " at least personal," because there may be higher modes of

God's existence of which all this tells us nothing. What I am claiming is that we cannot do justice to what we do know and feel in the act of reflection, if we use less than personal language. And so we are going to be led past pantheism to a religion of personal quality.

There is much to be said about this stage in the argument. But our previous analysis of science in chapter 2 and its relation to persons in chapter 3 has prepared the way for most of it. We have seen, for example, how the pictures of science, its models, and its interpretations, are concepts in the minds of people, so that science only exists because there are people, and the whole of its working is bound up with persons. Man and Nature have been bound together in an inescapable intimacy. No account of Nature can be given other than in personal terms. "The universe begins to look more like a great thought than like a great machine," said Jeans;[11] "Mind no longer appears as an accidental intruder into the realm of matter; we are beginning to suspect that we ought rather to hail it as the creator and governor of the realm of matter—not of course our individual minds, but the mind in which the atoms out of which our individual minds have grown, exist as thoughts . . . we discover that the universe shows evidence of a designing or controlling power that has something in common with our own individual minds . . . we are not so much strangers or intruders in the universe as we first thought."

It is not only the physical scientists who say this. Thus Julian Huxley in his latest book[12] on evolution, concludes that "The primacy of human personality has been . . . a *postulate* both of Christianity and of liberal democracy; but it is a *fact* of evolution. By whatever objective standard we choose to take, properly developed human personalities are the highest products of evolution."

So that which is given us is given in personal terms. This is the cement which holds our various disciplines together in one unity. It means that those things which we experience in science, those hidden harmonies of nature which we try to express within our concepts, are " an innermost circle . . . in which the personification of pure truth is no longer disguised by human ideologies and desires."[13]

To realise this personal character of everything that we see and touch and handle is to undergo an internal revolution. For our attitude to " things " when they are regarded simply as things, is vastly different from our attitude to persons. Everyone knows the story of the hard-boiled sceptic who was taken to see Madame Tussaud's waxworks in Marylebone Road, London; how he began his tour with the grudging admission that " this figure of a policeman does look pretty lifelike, but an expert can still spot the deficiencies," and how he collapsed when the figure responded to his remarks by very gently raising one eyebrow.[14] It may be an apocryphal story, but there is no doubt about the queer shock which we get when we discover that what we've taken to be a thing is living. I believe that the act of reflection, by showing us the personal character of reality, profoundly affects our relationship to it. Even the stars are different. When Caroline Herschel, sister of the famous William, wrote to the French astronomer

Aubert: I found, last night, at 16h. 24m. sidereal time, a comet, and do not know what to do with it "; and to the Greenwich astronomer Maskelyne: "I beg favour of you to take it under your protection,"[15] she was reacting to her environment in the same personal way as Carlyle after the loss of the pages of his " French Revolution," or as St. Francis in his " Canticle to the Sun."

This new relationship to our environment is not restricted to physical and chemical nature: it includes people. We have already seen this in chapter 2 when we discussed the rôle of the scientific community in science, and recognised that science could not exist except as a corporate activity, compassing all our work and binding us together, subject to a common ethos and tradition. The words which Dame Sybil Thorndike used about acting:[16] " If you are an actor, everybody has a part in you," apply equally about science, and show us how deeply it is impregnated with personal character. I believe we can go even further, and interpret the aspect of beauty which we have seen to be present as a regulating influence in science, as implying something about the nature of reality, and linking that which is given to us in science with some of the deepest elements in man's spiritual experience. For the beautiful, said Eric Gill,[17] " is holiness visible, holiness seen, heard, touched, holiness tasted—' O taste and see how gracious the Lord is '—holiness, smell of Paradise."

To recognise the personal character of reality is to be changed. This means that—if we may return for a moment to the discussion in chapter 3—it was not really sufficient to take Descartes' *cogito, ergo sum,* and add to it Heinemann's *respondeo, ergo sum.* It was certainly correct to make the addition, but we must go on further, in order that we may do justice to the personal relationships which we have seen to be so central. Professor Rosenstock-Huessy has urged that this extra keynote can be put in the form *respondeo, etsi mutabor*—I respond, although I shall be changed.[18] To face up to the totality of what we experience in our environment—both natural objects and human beings—in the act of reflection, is to risk the almost certain chance of being changed. We have come back again to what I said in the last chapter—"religion is man's total response to all his environment." If all this is given to us, if it is, in Bragg's phrase, "something revealed and not something imagined," then I do not see how to avoid the conclusion that our insight reflects the nature and character of Him from whom it comes. The argument may not be logically convincing, but at very least it is plausible to use the famous words from Newton's "Opticks":

> Does it not appear from Phaenomena that there is a Being incorporeal, living, intelligent, omnipresent, who in infinite space, as it were in his sensory, sees the things intimately and thoroughly perceives them, and comprehends them wholly by their immediate presence to himself?

Our New Testament puts it in much the same way —"In Him we live and move and have our being." The truth of the matter is that, having come to that which we can call God, we have found that nothing less than personal terms can be used to describe either the way, or the truth, or the life.

There are two temptations which may easily beset us when we have got this far. One is to place too high a value on knowledge (and science): the other is to place too little. Few of us can hope to have personal experience of more than a relatively small number of the "sections of our building," but that is no bar to the realisation of God. In the lovely words of Lancelot Andrewes:

> If by knowledge only, and reason, we could come to God, then none should come but they that are learned and have good wits, and so the way to God should be as if many should go on one journey, and because some can climb over hedges and thorns, therefore the way should be made over hedges and thorns. But God hath made His way "viam regiam"—the King's highway.

At the other extreme, we deny it or at best we damn it with faint praise.

> Life is a vale, its paths are dark and rough
> Only because we do not know enough:
> When science has discovered something more
> We shall be happier than we were before.[19]

These are both warnings. Few of us in university life escape the need to remember them from time to time.

But there is another and more subtle trap into which we may easily fall. This is to say that we accept science as the revelation of God, given by Himself; but then to sentimentalise about it, and fail to see within it the strong clash of colour and emotion which are part of its real essence. Let me illustrate what I mean. A few years ago I was sitting in my study, then just outside London, and watching the birds on the lawn outside my window. There were two sparrows engaged in love-play on the garden hose. How idyllic! How indicative of God's nature, we may be tempted to say; and many do say. But wait a moment, our picture of God cannot be painted so easily; the paleness of water-colours is not strong enough for God's delineation. There are some other birds by the side of those two sparrows; and these others are busily engaged in eating up thousands and thousands of little flying ants which have just hatched out of their eggs and are learning to move along the blades of grass. The French entomologist Fabre has put on record the ghoulish story of the predatory wasps, and the fiendish nuptial rites of the Praying Mantis; and this should remind us that our picture of God must resemble more the violence of a sunset painting by Turner than, as one of my friends once put it, a watery wash by a maiden aunt! Nature is red in tooth and claw; and if in the end we come to accept Fabre's own verdict on his studies, that all nature is " obedient to a sublime law of sacrifice," we shall mostly have to come to it in travail of soul. To make the act of reflection to the whole of our environment is to be led into the deeps, if only we manage to avoid being merely sentimental or trivial. The scientists may be some of God's heralds, but they are messengers of flaming fire.

What else could we expect if there is a wholeness and unity in life, and if science must reflect the nature of persons? For it is our universal human experience that we know both the wretchedness and greatness of human life, the exaltation and abasement of the human spirit. A recent writer has said that if we would properly apprehend our continuity with the Greek past, we must bring to our study a feeling both " violent and tender, full of reverence, excitement and joy." And those who would see God in science must be prepared for a tumultuous experience. Indeed they will the more readily accept what science shows if they have been brought up on *Pilgrim's Progess,* surely one of the most violent and tender of all books. The early Christian martyr answering the Roman centurion's " what's your God doing now?" with the calm reply, " hammering another nail in your emperor's coffin"; and the Methodist soldier saint John Haime who, after his horse was shot under him at the battle of Fontenoy, could answer his officer's " Haime, where is your God now?" with the equally confident riposte : " Sir, He is here with me," are on the way to see how the picture and revelation of science hold these dual elements which I have called " wretchedness and greatness." We are not permitted to have the one without the other also. Only the fear and blindness of many Christians have converted this specifically Christian revelation into anything different in quality from this.

Of course there is splendour : and if we will, we can sing Angela Morgan's poem :

I am aware
As I go commonly sweeping a stair

. . . . . .

I am aware of a splendour that ties
All the things of the earth to the things of the skies;
Here in my body the heavenly heat,
Here in my flesh the melodious beat
Of the planets that circle Divinity's feet.

But that is only half the picture. For evolution, the story of man, traced for us by the scientist, is seen as the travail of God's energy, creating man in His own image. No wonder it is shot through with pain and sacrifice and blood, like the travail of a woman with child. All things may be part of a great design; but it is a living, growing, developing pattern, if God is in it. Here, and only here, is the beginning of our understanding of that "sublime law of sacrifice" which Fabre saw throughout the animal world; and, no less, of that "groaning" of the whole physical creation which St. Paul has described for us in his letter to the Romans. For creation, and Nature, and man, these are not what God did, or even what God does, but what He is. The only interpretation that will do justice to them is in terms of love and sacrifice, linking them all together in the bond of God's Being.

If what I have been saying so far is correct, then man and nature share a common quality, springing from a common inheritance. To reflect and receive and respond, this is to be changed in our relationship to nature. Recent psychological studies have underlined this in no uncertain way. Without a proper relationship to our environment we cannot find any true fulfilment: and this involves the whole of our environment, so far as we can see it, both nature and God. Another way of putting this is to say that no one can be fully healthy without a response to his environment of the kind that we have called religious. One of the most remarkable developments of recent years has been the way in which this simple situation has been rediscovered by scientists. Let me quote two examples, one from a psychologist and the other from a mathematician-philosopher.

A few years ago Professor Jung summed up his life's experience in the following words: [20]

> During the past thirty years people from all the civilised countries of the earth have consulted me. . . . Among all my patients in the second half of life—that is to say over thirty-five--there has not been one whose problem in the last resort was not that of finding a religious outlook on life. It is safe to say that every one of them fell ill because he had lost that which the living religions of every age have given to their followers, and none of them has been really healed who did not regain his religious outlook.

My other illustration is from some recent words by Bertrand Russell," who is thinking of the influences that seem to be effective in vitalising human behaviour, and who summarises his feelings in this touchingly simple fashion:

There are certain things that our age needs, and

certain things it should avoid. It needs compassion, and a wish that mankind should be happy: it needs the desire for knowledge and the determination to eschew pleasant myths; it needs, above all, courageous hope and the impulse to creativeness. . . . The root of the matter is a very simple and old-fashioned thing, a thing so simple that I am almost ashamed to mention it for fear of the derisive smile with which wise cynics will greet my words. The thing I mean—please forgive me for mentioning it—is love, Christian love, or compassion. If you feel this, you have a motive for existence, a guide in action, a reason for courage, an imperative necessity for intellectual honesty.

So, from the pattern shown by science, we have been led to the relatedness of nature and ourselves, and to the source of much of the frustration of our lives—a false relation to our environment, and to Him in whom it finds its deepest meaning.

If it be said that we have gone far beyond our starting point, there is a sense in which we must agree : for the act of reflection on which we have continually insisted, carries with it a challenge and obligation that we can only shirk by drawing a veil between ourselves and what we see. But there is another sense in which many of the qualities inherent in the practice of science can still be traced, a guarantee of the wholeness of the view which I am putting forward. It is still true, for example, in Roger Bacon's phrase, that "of the three ways of acquiring knowledge—authority, reasoning and experience—only the last is effective": and certainly it was out of much and varied experience that Bertrand Russell and Jung were speaking. What we may call the "verification from experience" is central to my whole argument. When Alfred Noyes[22] says of his father: "If ever I had any doubts about the fundamental realities of religion, they could always be dispelled by one memory—the light upon my father's face as he came back from early Communion"; and when my old friend Dr. Alex Wood the Cambridge physicist writes in a letter to an inquirer: "What I really feel is that Christ has verified Himself in my experience, and that He can do in yours,"[23] there can be traced the authentic note of scientific inquiry. We are still in the same world as that in which we began—or, rather, we have enlarged that world but without breaking away from it.

This is the place at which the specifically Christian element is most naturally introduced. If it be true that truth can only be expressed in personal terms, and if it be true that all partial truths have a link which binds them together in the response of persons to God as He is revealed in the panorama of their environment, then it is not unreasonable to suppose that the whole process may be gathered up in one person—a representative person, an archetype—in whom the truths of nature and the truths of people find their meaning. Scientific laws are practically meaningless to a man who has not experienced them in some particular instance: it is because I see *this* stone fall that I realise the meaning of the law of gravity. As Collingwood says: "a universal truth is only true as realised in a particular instance; the

universal must be incarnate in the individual." The
Christian claims that this event has taken place in
Christ. He does not take away, or modify, the things
we have already concluded; but He comes to interpret for us the meaning of those generalities that I
have so far been discussing in this chapter. We can
say that He was needed, in Robert Browning's
phrase, to put a face on God : to be the type of perfection, to gather up in Himself the whole order of
nature, "both things on earth and things in
Heaven"; and the Christian asserts that in the living
present moment which we described in the last
chapter, He is experienced directly by the "I." This
cannot be proved in any logical sense, but it is all of
a piece with much of what we have been saying
about science, the primacy of experience and the
verification-in-experience of the truth of whatever
concept has been given to us in our encounter with
reality. For reasons which were explained in the last
chapter, science has no dealings with the I-God meeting : but with the Me-God situation it has much to
say, and we have seen some of it in the quotations
from Jung and Russell in the last few pages. The
religious activity of science becomes part of religion
and religion is recognised by me as an experience
which I have, whereby I feel myself confronted in
some utterly personal way by the spiritual quality of
the whole Universe. Why then can I not say:
"Christ lives in me," and do justice to this experience? St. Paul, and all the saints, have said it; and
many of them were people most evidently whole in
their attitude to their environment. Some of them
we have known ourselves, and, at least for them, we

dare not separate their convictions expressed in words
like these, from the wholeness—or holiness—of their
lives as seen by others. " We can find our right place
in the Being that envelops us only if we experience in
our individual lives the universal life which wills and
rules within it. The nature of the living Being without me I can understand only through the living
Being which is within me."[24] If I cannot face the
implications of the Being without me, as it is seen in
science, without some act of response and the possibility of being changed, it is scarcely surprising that
those who really face the fact of Christ hardly ever
emerge unscathed. In Him much that we have seen
before, finds its concrete expression: for He is the
truth of God and His is the beauty of holiness; He is
God's fulness, " the fulness of Him that filleth all in
all "; in Him we see in its plainest form the wretchedness and greatness of life, and are led to a new
interpretation of the inner meaning of suffering and
sacrifice. Living the good life is not an eternal
struggle to balance conflicting claims of science, art,
poetry, philanthropy and ritual, as though these
warred against each other like the tribes of Anglo-
Saxon Britain; living the good life means receiving all
these partial revelations, reflecting upon them and
responding to them. So it is that truth, wonder, worship, faith form a quartet, in which the fulness of
each separate element lies in its relation to the rest.
We can receive the particular revelation in science
and rejoice to call it a work of the Holy Spirit; we
can see how it has its part to play in the perfecting
of the pattern dimly glimpsed in science and more

clearly etched in the life and teaching of Jesus Christ; we begin to understand how "it is your Father's good pleasure to give you the Kingdom"; and how, until a man has entered into the new relationship which follows his response to what he has seen, he does not partake fully of the promises of God.

There are many ways by which men may come to this new birth : and it ill behoves any of us to deny or belittle the progress that our neighbour has made; not all who cry "Lord, Lord" will get first places in the Kingdom. Many of those who call them-selves scientists will never be able to use these words meaningfully, yet I believe most firmly that they may be said to be religious. " In science," said Eddington, " we sometimes have convictions which we cherish, but cannot justify; we are influenced by some innate sense of the fitness of things." Or, in some famous words of the philosopher F. H. Bradley :

> Some in one way, and some in others, we seem to touch and have communion with what is beyond the visible world. In various manners we find something higher, which both supports and humbles, both chastens and transports us. And with certain persons the intellectual effort to under-stand the Universe is a principal way of thus ex-periencing the Deity.

Such people are not likely to be sustained, as the astronomer Kepler was sustained, by the thought that as they work they are "thinking God's thoughts after Him." But I believe that we may fairly tell

them that that is indeed what they are doing. Most
of them will agree that for them "science is an
imaginative adventure of the mind seeking truth in a
world of mystery";[25] and surely we can start with
them there, as we started in these pages, and gradually be led to a wider awareness. At least we can tell
them that they will not be obliged to renounce that
which they do already possess. For in Canon Raven's
words, we must show them that "life abundant is
both the goal of evolution and the purpose of
Christ," and that "for mankind there are two unique
sacraments which disclose the meaning and convey
the experience of reality: they are the created universe and the person of Jesus Christ."

But there are others who will come into their religious experience with hardly any intellectual aid.
They too can enter into the wonder and the power of
a renewed life. "I wish," said Bishop Berkeley,
"that our opinions were fairly stated and submitted
to the judgment of men who had plain common
sense, without the prejudices of a learned education."
It was a hard word, but it was needed. For although
a learned education, even in science, is for most of us
a means of getting our living and playing our part
in the wider community, "it is only a means, not
living itself. One great mistake of modern man is to
worry too much about his means of living—his
models and his comparisons. We must go on making
them and we can greatly enjoy doing so. They are a
chief glory of our way of life, but they are not the
whole of life. A fine morning, a good meal, work
well done and a pleasant sleep, these are as truly our
life as is talking about them. We can enjoy life and,

like the birds, we must sing about it. . . . The plants and the sky and the stars do not sing or talk, but are not the less real for that."[26] And those of us who have, in however small a way, sensed the satisfactions of seeing God in both aspects, will want to help others. We shall certainly feel the strength of Jung's advice : " Nobody can really understand these things unless he has experienced them himself. I am therefore much more interested in pointing out ways to such experience than in devising intellectual formulae which, for lack of experience, must necessarily remain an empty web of words."[27] This is why our Lord gathered His disciples with the simple word : " Come "; and why, in their turn, His followers have said " O taste and see."

I have come to the end of my exposition. And when I pause to see the immensity of the claims which I have made, I confess that I am almost bewildered at the thought that these things can really be. For we began wondering what place, if any, could be granted to religion in a scientific age like ours : we went on to analyse science and concluded that both by its actual practice and from the nature of its presuppositions, it was none other than a religious activity. But its truth was bound up with persons, and the account that it gave was ineluctably linked with the human mind. Science was not alone in this, for other revelations of reality owned the same quality. The act of reflection enabled us to see how all separate disciplines were one, with spiritual and personal character, confronting us with reality and challenging us, each in our way, to make a total response to the whole of our environment. Here

science is needed to show us things which otherwise
we could never know—of the grandeur of time and
space, and the strange sweet harmony of things. But,
alone, it is not enough. Fcr we live among our
fellows, and we can make sense of our relationship
to them, and of their human needs, only in terms
of a God, partly seen in science, and in art and history and philosophy; partly experienced in wholly
personal terms in the "living present"; and verified
in the power of a transformed life. In the lovely
words of Thomas Traherne, the seventeenth-century
mystic: [28]

> He that knows the secrets of nature with Albertus
> Magnus, or the motions of the heavens with Gali-
> leo, or the cosmography of the moon with Hevelius,
> or the body of man with Galen, or the nature of
> diseases with Hippocrates, or the harmonies in
> melody with Orpheus, or of poetry with Homer, or
> of grammar with Lily, or of whatever else with the
> greatest artist; he is nothing if he knows them
> merely for talk or idle speculation, or transient
> and external use. But he that knows them for
> value, and knows them his own, shall profit infi-
> nitely.

We should hardly have dared to ask all this for ourselves, but, like our science, it is given. To see this,
and to recognise it as all of a piece, is to enter the
Kingdom of Heaven, and to initiate an experience
whose fulfilment lies beyond time and space. All life
is sacramental; all nature is needed that Christ should
be understood: Christ is needed that all nature

should be seen as holy; that amid all its turbulence
and tumult God's perfection might grow; and our
hearts be filled with wonder at the significance of the
least of all this work.

> What does it take to make a rose,
>   Mother mine?
> It takes the world's eternal wars,
> It takes the moon and all the stars,
> It takes the might of heaven and hell
> And the everlasting love as well,
>   Little child.[29]

NOTES AND REFERENCES

CHAPTER I

1. *Experience and Interpretation*, Cambridge University Press, 1953, p. 10.
2. *Nature, Man and God*, Macmillan, 1934, p. 306.
3. Quoted by C. E. Raven, *Science and Religion*, Cambridge University Press, 1953, p. 101.
4. *Modern Cosmology and the Christian Idea of God*, Oxford University Press, 1952, p. 1.
5. *Science and the Common Understanding*, Oxford University Press, 1954, p. 1.
6. *The Neglect of Science*, Basil Blackwell, Oxford, 1951.
7. Quoted by Bernard Barber, *Science and the Social Order*, George Allen and Unwin, 1953, p. 133.
8. *The Origins of Modern Science*, by H. Butterfield, Bell & Sons, 1949, p. viii.
   Science and the Modern World, 1927, and *Religion in the Making*, 1926, A. N. Whitehead, Cambridge University Press.
9. *Question*, 1954, **6**, p. 116.
10. *The Future of an Illusion*, L. & V. Woolf, for the Institute of Psycho-Analysis, 1929, p. 68.
11. *The Transformation of the Scientific World View*, S.C.M. Press, English translation, 1953, p. 27.
12. F. S. C. Northrop, of Yale, quoted in *Physics Today*, Jan. 1954, p. 9, from his book *The Taming of the Nations*.
13. *The Scientific Attitude*, Penguin Books, 1941, pp. 124, 66.
14. Quoted by W. R. R. Ball, *A History of Mathematics*, Macmillan, 1924 edition, p. 169.
15. See *Notes and Records of the Royal Society*, 1952, **10**, 15.
16. In *Science and Ethics* (edited by C. H. Waddington), Allen & Unwin, 1942, p. 114, quoted by W. A. Whitehouse,

Christian Faith and the Scientific Attitude, Oliver & Boyd, Edinburgh, 1952, p. 111.

17. For these and further relevant quotations, see *Man and his Gods*, by Homer W. Smith, English edition by Jonathan Cape, 1953, p. 371.

18. The proposal to form a British Association was made by a clergyman, two of its first three presidents were in holy orders, and the historian of that first meeting in 1831 wrote that ' to the Church, the British Association is deeply indebted.'

19. Quoted by K. Heim, *Christian Faith and Natural Science*, English translation published by S.C.M. Press, 1953, p. 13.

20. See Fr. F. Copleston, *A History of Philosophy*, Burns Oates, 1950, vol. 2, p. 220.

21. Translations into English of volumes 4 and 5 are listed in references 11 and 19.

22. Reference (19), p. 33.

23. Reference (11), p. 11.

24. Reference (4), p. 157.

25. See S. Bondi, *Cosmology*, Cambridge University Press, 1952, and F. Hoyle, *The Nature of the Universe*, Basil Blackwell, Oxford, 1950.

26. For a sharp attack on this intrusion of metaphysical notions into modern cosmology, see H. Dingle, *Monthly Notices Roy. Astron. Soc.*, 1953, **113**, 393.

27. *Christian Faith and the Scientific Attitude*, by W. A. Whitehouse, Oliver & Boyd, Edinburgh, 1952, p. 121.

28. Reference (4), p. 156.

29. Professor E. N. da C. Andrade, in *The Listener*, 10 July 1947.

30. *Some Aspects of the Conflict between Science and Religion*, by Prof. H. H. Price, Cambridge University Press, 1953, p. 1.

31. *New Frontiers of the Mind*, 1937, *The Reach of the Mind*, Faber & Faber, 1948.

32. This facility is much more common than is sometimes

supposed. I myself knew a girl who was able to write down correctly all but one of a series of about fifteen shapes exhibited in a radio experiment during the 1930s. But she has never attempted to develop this power.

33. J. Stafford Wright, in *The Christian Graduate*, 1952, **4,** p. 128.

34. *Confessions*, Book XI.

35. *The Principles of Human Knowledge.* See e.g. an article by G. J. Whitrow, *British Journal for the Philosophy of Science*, 1953, **4,** 13.

36. An excellent account is by Sir Edmund Whittaker; *From Euclid to Eddington*, Cambridge University Press, 1949.

CHAPTER II

1. F. M. Heywood, *Education and the Spirit*, reprinted in *Religion in Education*, S.C.M. Press, 1954, **21,** 45.

2. *The Common Sense of Science*, Heinemann, 1951, p. 100.

3. *A Scientific Autobiography*, Williams & Norgate, 1950, Chapter 3.

4. See e.g. J. Z. Young, *Doubt and Certainty in Science*, Oxford University Press, 1951.

5. D. McKie and G. R. de Beer, *Notes and Records of the Royal Society of London*, 1951, **9,** 46.

6. *Modern Science and Modern Man*, Columbia University Press, New York, 1952.

7. C. F. Powell, *Proc. Roy. Soc. A.*, 1954, **221,** 278.

8. *Virtue in Our Time*, by Alan Pryce-Jones, *The Listener*, 1953, p. 996.

9. Quoted by R. B. Haldane in his Gifford Lectures for 1903-4, *The Pathway to Reality*, John Murray, p. 127.

10. Quoted by K. R. Popper, in *The Listener*, 1954, p. 291.

11. *The Listener*, 5 March 1953, p. 379.

12. *The Art of Scientific Investigation*, Heinemann, 1950, p. 145.

13. *Synopsis Quadrupedum*, p. 46, quoted by C. E. Raven, *Science and Religion*, Cambridge University Press, 1951, p. 120.

14. *Opera* (Horsley's Edition) iv., p. 437, quoted by H. Dingle, reference (26) of chapter 1.

15. See Reference (4).

16. For a discussion of this topic, see reference (4), p. 152 and references quoted therein.

17. *The Four Gospels*, a new translation by E. V. Rieu, Penguin Books, 1952, p. xxv.

18. *Opticks*, Fourth Edition, p. 337.

19. *Natural Science and the Spiritual Life*, Oxford University Press, 1951.

20. Reference (26) of chapter 1, p. 407.

21. Reference (3), p. 109.

22. Reference (2), p. 3.

23. C. Lanczos, *The Variational Principles of Mechanics*, University of Toronto Press, 1949, p. ix.

24. Quoted in his Obituary Notice, *Proc. Phys. Soc. London*, A, 1949, **62**, 857.

25. *J. Chem. Soc. London*, 1947, p. 1277.

26. See reference (2), pp. 7-10.

27. *A History of History*, Columbia University Press, 1939.

28. Ludwig von Bertalanffy, *Problems of Life*, Watts & Co., 1952, p. 194.

29. Published for the University of Durham by the Oxford University Press.

30. Quoted from *William Herschel* by J. B. Sidgwick, Faber & Faber, 1953, p. 124.

31. *From Euclid to Eddington*, Cambridge University Press, 1949, p. 4.

32. E. G. Cox and J. A. G. Smith, *Nature*, 1954, **173**, 75.

33. This is one of the chief conclusions of Mr. Barber's book, reference (7) of chapter 1.

34. See *The Listener*, 28 Jan. 1954, p. 170.

35. *The Life of Science*, Henry Schuman, New York, 1948.

36. Reference (7) of chapter 3.

37. See reference (3), p. 187.

CHAPTER III

1. *Religion in the Making*, p. 155-6.
2. Psalm 24, v. 1.
3. *Some Religious Illusions in Art, Literature and Experience*, by Sir Ernest Kellaway, Watts & Co., 1953, p. 3.
4. *Do What You Will*, Thinker's Library, Watts & Co., 1936.
5. *The Facts of Life*, George Allen & Unwin, 1953, p. 302.
6. *Man and His Gods*, Jonathan Cape, 1953, p. 6.
7. *The Study of Instinct*, Oxford University Press, 1951.
8. *Cell and Psyche*, University of North Carolina Press, 1950, p. 107.
9. *Man on His Nature*, Cambridge University Press, 1940.
10. See, for example, *The Physical Basis of Mind*, edited by P. Laslett, Basil Blackwell, Oxford, 1950, where almost all the underlying philosophy, except that of Gilbert Ryle, seems to be at fault in this respect.
11. *The Philosophy of Physical Science*, Cambridge University Press, 1939.
12. J. C. Eccles, 1951, **168**, 53.
13. From p. 64 of *Contemporary Mind*, compiled by J. W. N. Sullivan, Humphrey Toulmin, 1934.
14. *The Concept of Mind*, Hutchinson, 1949.
15. I have developed this at greater length in my Riddell Lectures, *Christianity in an Age of Science*, Oxford University Press, 1953, p. 22.
16. See reference (3) in chapter 2 of this book, p. 73.
17. Quoted on p. 177 of reference (3) of chapter 1.
18. Reference (9), pp. 78-79.
19. See reference (1) of chapter 1, pp. 137-8.
20. Quoted in reference (8), p. 47.
21. See C. F. von Weiszäcker, *The World View of Physics*, English translation published by Routledge and Kegan Paul, London, 1952, p. 2.
22. Quoted by Sir Harold Hartley, *Nature*, 1953, **171**, 1045.

23. *Concepts out of Context*, Science News No. 25, Penguin Books, 1952.

24. *Nature*, 1954, **173**, 113.

25. J. W. Rowntree, *Claim your Inheritance*, Bannisdale Press, 1949.

26. *Philosophic Problems of Nuclear Science*, English translation, Faber & Faber, 1952, p. 107.

27. But compare J. L. Stocks, *Reason and Intuition*, quoted by C. E. Raven on p. 32 of reference (1) of chapter 1. He begins 'Religious belief is a total assertion which has for its subject the whole world order.' Similar ideas however have been expressed by many others. For example: H. Butterfield, *Christianity and History*, Bell & Sons, 1949, p. 22, Religion is 'the way we decide to set our personalities for the purpose of meeting the whole stream of events.' And A. N. Whitehead, *Science and the Modern World*, Cambridge University Press, 1927, chapter XII, 'Religion is the reaction of human nature to its search for God.' Also D. Bonhoeffer, *Letters and Papers from Prison*, English translation, S.C.M. Press, 1954, p. 167, 'The religious act is always something partial; faith' (i.e. religion itself as distinct from any particular religious act) 'is always something whole, an act involving the whole life.' But I believe that my own form of words is the most appropriate for our present purposes.

28. Quoted from *Colin Maclaurin*, by H. W. Turnbull, J. of the Glasgow Mathematical Association, **1**, No. 4, June 1953.

29. See *Nature*, 1953, **171**, 1035.

30. *William Herschel*, by J. B. Sidgwick, Faber & Faber, 1953, pp. 81, 82.

31. Reference (4) of chapter 2.

32. Reference (25) of chapter 1.

33. Reference (26), p. 210.

34. *The Physical Basis of Life*, Routledge & Kegan Paul, 1951.

35. *The History of Nature*, English Translation, Routledge & Kegan Paul, 1951, p. 13.

36. *Space, Time and Gravitation*, Cambridge University Press, 1920, p. 131.

37. *Toward a Philosophy of History*, by J. Ortega y Gasset (translated H. Weyl), New York: W. W. Norton, 1941, p. 165.

38. *British Journal for the Philosophy of Science*, 1953, **4**, 244.

39. *The Everlasting Man*, Hodder & Stoughton, 1925, chapter 1.

CHAPTER IV

1. *De Augmentis*, iii.

2. *Science and the Adventure of Living*.

3. *The Listener*, 22 Jan. 1953, p. 147.

4. *The British Association—a Retrospect*, by O. J. R. Howarth, 1931, p. 20.

5. *Proc. Roy. Soc.* B., 1953, **141**, 511.

6. See *Nature*, 1954, **173**, 416.

7. Sainte-Beuve, quoted by Alan Pryce-Jones, *The Listener*, 26 No. 1953, p. 905.

8. See *Friends Intelligencer*, 1 Oct. 1949. I am indebted to Dr. H. T. Gillett for this most interesting quotation.

9. Reference (27) in chapter 1, pp. 131 and 15.

10. *Faith and Its Psychology*, Duckworth & Co., 1919, p. 197.

11. *The Mysterious Universe*, Cambridge University Press, 1931, p. 137.

12. *Evolution in Action*, 1953.

13. Reference (26) of chapter 3, p. 119.

14. *Where Science and Faith Meet*, Inter-Varsity Fellowship, 1953, p. 21.

15. Quoted in reference (30) of chapter 3.

16. A lecture at the Old Vic, London, 8 Jan. 1954, reported in the *Manchester Guardian*, 9 Jan. 1954, p. 4.

17. *Last Essays*, Jonathan Cape, 1942, p. 81.

18. See the fuller account of this by Dr. J. H. Oldham, in *Question*, 1953, **6**, 84.

19. Newdigate poem *On the Benefit of the Electric Light*, by Hilaire Belloc.

20. Quoted by R. J. Z. Werblowsky in *The Listener*, 23 April 1953, p. 677.

21. *Impact of Science on Society*, George Allen & Unwin, 1952, p. 114.

22. From his autobiography—*Two Worlds for Memory*, Sheed & Ward, 1953.

23. From the first Alex Wood Memorial Lecture, Fellowship of Reconciliation, 38, Gordon Square, London, W.C.1, p. 20.

24. *My Life and Thought*, by Albert Schweitzer, Allen & Unwin, 1933.

25. Presidential address of Sir Cyril Hinshelwood to 1953 conference of Science Masters Association, at Oxford.

26. Reference (4) in chapter 2, pp. 162-3.

27. C. S. Jung, *Two Essays on Analytical Psychology*, Routledge & Kegan Paul, 1953.

28. Meditation, No. 341 from his *Centuries of Meditations*.

29. Alfred Noyes, *The Forest of Wild Thyme*, Wm. Blackwood & Son, 1905.

INDEX

Other Fontana Religious Books

MERE CHRISTIANITY

C. S. Lewis. Here at a popular price is a revised and amplified edition of C. S. Lewis's three famous books, *Broadcast Talks, Christian Behaviour,* and *Beyond Personality,* brilliantly presenting the author's modern revaluations of Christian apologetics, ethics and theology.

THE SCREWTAPE LETTERS

C. S. Lewis. This witty and profound analysis of Christian strength and weaknesses outlined in the letters of the elderly devil Screwtape to his young nephew, is a classic of religious exposition.

THE PROBLEM OF PAIN

C. S. Lewis. The author gives his view as a layman on the Christian doctrine relating to all aspects of the problem of pain and explains the existence of pain in a Christian world.
"It is really a pleasure to be able to praise a book unreservedly and that is just what I can do with this book."
Manchester Guardian

THE DIVINE PITY

Gerald Vann, O.P. Doubters as well as professing Christians who look for a strong simple statement of the abiding truths of Christianity will find inspiration from this work.

THE PLAIN MAN LOOKS AT THE BIBLE

William Neil. This book is meant for the plain man who would like to know what to think about the Bible to-day. It deals with the relevance of the Bible and restates its message for the Twentieth Century.

THE GOSPELS IN MODERN ENGLISH

J. B. Phillips. "It is all to the good that we should be given a translation in straightforward English, and Mr. Phillips has a flair for doing this that none of his predecessors in the task seem to have had."
Times Literary Supplement

Fontana books make available in attractive, readable yet inexpensive editions, the best books of religious thought and learning.

If you would like to be kept informed of new and forthcoming titles please apply to your local bookseller or write to

WILLIAM COLLINS SONS AND CO. LTD.,
144 Cathedral Street, Glasgow, C.4.